FROM RED LETTER CHA

# BEING
KIDS

## CHALLENGE

A 40-DAY CHALLENGE TO
BE LIKE JESUS

# ZACH AND ALLISON ZEHNDER
### WITH
## DOUG PETERSON

# ACKNOWLEDGMENTS

I would like to express special thanks of gratitude:

To PlainJoe Studios and Doug Peterson. Your tireless work on this project: writing, editing, designing and illustrating has always been above and beyond any expectations.

To Steven and Susan Blount and Quadrivium Group. Your continued dedication and faith in this project has given us great confidence to finish well.

To Andrea, our dear friend and co-conspirator in this crazy journey. Thank you for all you have done for Red Letter Challenge.

To my husband Zach, the boldest and most faithful follower to the call of God that I know. Not every couple is called to work as closely together as we do and I am honored to be able to do life with you.

I would like to dedicate this book to our godchildren: Addison Thrasher, Brooke, Blaine and Alex Ganus, Sophia Hoeppner, Jada Baye and Joshua Fritsch. Jesus is far more real than anything you can see, hear or touch in this world and loves you more than you could ever imagine.

**"Now faith is the assurance of the things we hope for, being the proof of things we do not see and the convictions of their reality. " Hebrews 11:1**

## -ALLISON ZEHNDER

# TABLE OF

# CONT

# ENTS

# KEYSTONE HABITS

Michael Phelps is the greatest Olympian of all-time, with a record 23 gold medals and 28 Olympic medals in all. But his most amazing victory was in the 200-meter butterfly at the 2008 Games in Beijing.

When Phelps dove into the pool, his goggles became crooked and filled with water. The problem kept getting worse, and by the time Phelps reached the final turn, he couldn't see at all. But he didn't panic. His coach had trained him for just this problem by having him practice in a pitch-dark pool.

As Phelps made the last turn, the crowd was cheering wildly. But he didn't know if he was in the lead or if he had been passed. He began counting the strokes in his head—18, 19, 20...On the 21st stroke, his hand touched the edge of the pool. Then he ripped off his goggles and looked at the scoreboard. Beside his name were the letters "WR."

He not only won. He had just set a World Record!

# GOOD HABITS

The secret to Michael Phelps' success was his training habits, which kicked in and helped him when he was swimming blind in 2008.

Here were just some of Phelps' key training habits:

- He swam six hours a day for six days a week.

- Every breakfast, he ate eggs, oatmeal, and four high-calorie shakes. (Don't try this unless you're swimming six hours a day!)

- Before each race, he did the same warm-ups and stretches.

- He then put on headphones and listened to the same music.

- He closed his eyes and visualized every part of the upcoming race.

About 40 percent of what we do every day are not decisions. They're habits. A habit is something you do regularly, often without even thinking about it. Some habits are bad—picking your nose, for example. But some habits are good, especially the Keystone Habits.

Keystone Habits lead to all kinds of good things. Some examples of Keystone Habits are exercising regularly, being careful about what you eat, making your bed every morning, and flossing your teeth. Yes, making your bed leads to other good things! For example, it's been connected with being able to do your job better.

In this book, we're going to be looking at *spiritual* Keystone Habits.

# SPIRITUAL KEYSTONE HABITS

In our previous book, *Red Letter Challenge Kids,* we talked about five important areas of our life with Jesus—Being, Forgiving, Serving, Giving, and Going. This book narrows down our target to the first part—BEING like Jesus.

To do this, we've set five targets. We're taking aim at five Keystone Habits that Jesus practiced in His life. They are:

**FORM FRIENDSHIPS**
**STUDY SCRIPTURE**
**PAUSE TO PRAY**
**STOP FOR SOLITUDE**
**CHOOSE CHURCH**
} **KEYSTONE HABITS**

During the Warmup, on Days 1 through 5, we'll look at how each one of these five Keystone Habits played out in the life of Jesus. Then, on Days 6 through 40, we'll dive deeper into each one of the five spiritual habits.

These habits can change your life. Small habits done over a long time make a big difference. That's why most of the challenges over these 40 days are small—but powerful.

1 Corinthians 9:24-27 compares spiritual training to the training of an athlete. Verse 25 says, **"Everyone who competes in the games goes into strict training. They do it to get a crown that will not last, but we do it to get a crown that will last forever."**

Did you hear that? We're training to get a crown that will last forever! We're following Jesus, and our reward will be greater than any gold medal.

# A FEW LAST POINTS

### THE SANDS OF REDVALE
In our last book, *Red Letter Challenge Kids*, you met Aiden, Isabella, and Emily Perez, as they ventured to an incredible land called Redvale. The three Perez kids are back in this book with an all-new adventure that will build on the lessons we learn in *BEING Challenge Kids*.

The story begins on page 10 and continues throughout the book.

### RED ALERTS!
One of the characters in *The Sands of Redvale* is Red, a fox who speaks three languages. Scattered throughout this book, you'll find brief Red Alerts from Red the Fox, offering nuggets of information about the Bible.

### FIND TEAMMATES
Finally, *BEING Challenge Kids* was created to be experienced with others as a family, class, Sunday School, or youth group. We encourage you to find somebody with whom you can embark on this adventure.

Moses spent 40 days on the mountain before God gave him the Ten Commandments. Jesus also spent 40 days in the wilderness before he began His ministry. Let your 40 days begin now!

HAVE FUN COLORING THIS PAGE!
FIND MORE LIKE THIS AT BEINGCHALLENGE.COM/KIDS

# THE SANDS OF REDVALE

## PART 1

If things didn't change soon, Emily Perez was going to go crazy. It felt as if her entire world was falling to pieces.

Emily stood at the edge of their front lawn, staring out on the quiet neighborhood. She saw an older couple going for a walk, but when they neared someone else, they crossed to the other side of the street. The old couple had to stay at least six feet away from other people. So did everybody else on the planet.

There was no end in sight to the lockdown caused by the Covid-19 virus. The Florida governor had closed the schools and told everyone to stay away from others to avoid catching the virus sweeping the world. Now, loneliness was sweeping the world.

This was harder on Emily than anyone else she knew because she loved being with people. She hated being alone. She craved friends...and talking...and playing...anything but being cooped up in the house.

*Why was this happening?* Emily wondered every day.

"Hey, Em! Let's play some soccer!"

Emily spun around to see her brother, Aiden, strolling out the front door. He tossed a soccer ball up and down in his right hand.

"Go away. We just did that an hour ago," Emily said. Today, she was feeling really irritable. And no one seemed to irritate her more than Aiden.

The front door swung open again, and out stepped their older sister, Isabella. She plopped down on the front steps and leaned her head against her hand.

"Something wrong?" Aiden asked.

"Mom and Dad said I had to go out and get some fresh air. They even made me put away my phone."

"That must be hard," Emily said. "Your phone is like your best friend in the world."

Isabella made a face at her.

"Isabella, play some soccer with me!" Aiden said, as if he were leading a pep rally. But Isabella didn't look like she had even one drop of pep. She just sat there on the steps, like a lump.

"You're not the only one who hates this, Isabella," he added. "I should be out playing soccer with my buddies, but I'm stuck here."

"Stuck with *us* you mean?" Emily said, her irritation growing.

"Well…Yes."

Aiden dropped the ball on the grass and kicked it in Emily's direction. But she just watched it roll on past and into the street.

"Hey! I passed it to you! Go get the ball!" Aiden said.

"I told you I don't wanna play."

"And I said go get my ball."

He was really getting on her nerves. Emily ignored him and stormed toward the house. As she passed Aiden, he grabbed her by the arm, and she tried to shake loose. "Let go!"

"Not until you agree to get my ball!"

"Get it yourself!"

"Cut it out you two," said their big sister, trying to separate them. But Aiden wouldn't let go of Emily, and he latched his other hand onto Isabella.

"Oh no, my hands have superpower! They're super sticky, and I'm stuck to you two forever! FOR-EV-ER!" he shouted, emphasizing every syllable.

"Not funny," Emily said, squirming and thrashing, but Aiden still wouldn't let go. "LET GOOOOO!" Isabella also tried to break free, but she wasn't putting much effort into it, Emily thought.

"I can't let go! I told you my hands are super sticky! I'm Sticky Man!" Aiden pretended to try to shake his hands loose.

Suddenly, the front door opened and Emily sensed trouble.

"Aiden, let go of your sisters," came their father's voice. Loud and clear.

"But my hands have..."

*"Aiden,"* said their mom.

Obediently, Aiden finally let go, and Emily rubbed her arm, scowling at him.

"Since you're having so much trouble finding something to keep you busy, we've decided to *give* you something to do," said their father.

"You can all go inside and clean your rooms," added Mom.

A collective groan. "But Aiden was the one causing trouble," Isabella said.

"That's true!" Emily blurted.

It was obvious that Aiden got a kick out of getting on their nerves. *Why did she have to be stuck in the house with him?* Emily wondered.

"C'mon. Everyone inside," said Dad. "Start cleaning your room. And Emily, since you've got the messiest room, Aiden and Isabella will come help you once they've finished their rooms."

Another big groan.

Like prisoners, they marched inside and trudged to their rooms, which were on the second floor of the house. Emily looked around at her small bedroom. Clothes everywhere. Mom and Dad insisted she clean it every morning, so how could it get so messy in just one day?

She opened her closet and stared at the mounds of mess. Her idea of "cleaning" was jamming stuff into her closet. This was going to take all day to sort through! Emily gave a big sigh and turned away from the closet.

That's when she felt it. Something hit her on the back of the neck. Something small, almost like a drop of rain. Emily turned. Then blinked. Something struck her on the nose. A little particle of something. Then another speck shot out of the darkness and pinged against her forehead. Then...

*WOOOOOOOOSHHH!*

A blast of wind and sand roared out of her closet, hurling her backward against the wall. There was a sandstorm inside her closet!

Fighting the wind, Emily clawed her way back to the door of her closet and stared inside. All of her clothes and stuff inside the closet had disappeared. All she could see was a swirl of brown sand. She took several steps into the closet, leaning against the wind. She could no longer see the back wall, but she could make out something in the midst of the sand.

Something red.

It appeared to be a fox. A red fox. Was it her old friend, Red?

The fox was trying to tell her something, but she couldn't hear the words. He motioned for her to follow him, and she knew what that meant.

They were going back to Redvale.

# TO BE CONTINUED ON PAGE 38.

# THE WARMUP

INTRODUCING...

## FORM FRIENDSHIPS

## STUDY SCRIPTURE

## PAUSE TO PRAY

## STOP FOR SOLITUDE

## CHOOSE CHURCH

# DAY 1

## FORM FRIENDSHIPS

### FIRST KEYSTONE HABIT

When the Covid-19 virus spread across the world in 2020, people everywhere stayed in their homes as much as possible and kept six feet from people at stores. It was tough. That's because God created people to be with others—in small groups and big groups.

That's also why one of Jesus's spiritual habits was to Form Friendships.

When Jesus began His ministry, one of the first things He did was find people with whom to work and live. Jesus could have done His work alone. But He called the 12 disciples to follow Him because He knew we are not meant to be alone.

A "disciple" means a "learner" or "student." But the 12 disciples were not just Jesus's students. They were His friends.

### THE 12

When Jesus chose His 12 disciples, He didn't look for the popular, rich, or famous. He chose ordinary people. Some of them were even hated, such as Matthew the tax collector. The 12 disciples show us that very different people can get along— when they have Jesus at the center.

Here is the lineup of Jesus's friends. Color the picture of each disciple.

**Peter** was the first disciple to say that Jesus was the Messiah. He wrote two books of the Bible: 1 and 2 Peter.

**James** loved his brother John. They were often found working together. He was the first of the disciples to be put to death.

**John** and his brother James stuck together like glue. They were the "Sons of Thunder." He wrote five books of the Bible: Gospel of John, I John, II John, III John, and Revelation.

**Andrew** was the brother of Peter and a follower of John the Baptist.

**Matthew** was a tax collector. Tax collectors collected money from people to give to Rome (and kept a lot for themselves). He wrote the first book of the New Testament—the Gospel of Matthew.

**Simon** was very proud to be a Jew and worked hard for the rights of Jews. Simon loved Jesus and wanted everyone to know who He is.

**Philip** helped an Ethiopian man learn about the love of Jesus. When Jesus fed the multitudes, He tested Philip. He asked Philip where they could get bread for all of the people.

**Bartholomew** may have come from royal blood of noble birth. Some believe he was also known as Nathanael. He loved reading the Scripture. He was a missionary to Armenia.

**Thomas** was also called "Doubting Thomas" because he wouldn't believe Jesus was alive until he saw the nail prints in the Lord's hands. He then served as a missionary and traveled far away to tell others about Jesus.

**Thaddaeus** was also called Judas, son of James. He became a missionary and preached the Good News of Jesus to Assyria and Persia.

Don't confuse him with the other disciple named **James**! Some think he might be the one they called James the Younger, whose mother was among the women at Jesus's tomb. He may have written the Epistle of James in the Bible.

**Judas** was the treasurer and took care of the money. He betrayed Jesus for 30 pieces of silver.

# YOU'VE GOT A FRIEND

Who are the people you spend the most time with? You may not have 12 good friends like Jesus did, but that's OK.

Friends are important because the kinds of friends you surround yourself with shape who you are. On the three trading cards below, write the names of three people you spend the most time with and jot down a couple of things about them. They can be friends, family, classmates, or neighbors. If you'd like, also draw a picture of each person.

*On Days 6 through 12, we're going to learn more about why friendships are important and why it matters who you hang out with.*

# DAY 2
## STUDY SCRIPTURE

### KEYSTONE HABIT #2

Mary and Joseph were horrified. They were leaving Jerusalem after Passover, but they couldn't find their 12-year-old son, Jesus, anywhere. The city was packed with thousands of people who had come to celebrate. Can you imagine what your parents would think if they couldn't find you in a big city? It'd be terrifying.

When Mary and Joseph finally found Jesus, He was in the Temple, learning about the Scriptures from the rabbis (teachers). The story ends by saying, **"And Jesus grew in wisdom and stature, and in favor with God and man." Luke 2:52**

The Scriptures will do that. They will help you grow in amazing ways. And that's why Jesus's second spiritual habit was reading Scripture.

The Scriptures that Jesus read was the Old Testament—the first half of our Bible. (The New Testament didn't come until after Jesus.) He lived His life surrounded by Scripture.

### IN THE BEGINNING WAS THE WORD

If studying Scripture was an important habit of Jesus, then it's an important habit for us as well.

Studying Scripture is so important that Jesus memorized a big chunk of the Old Testament. When He spoke, He would quote many passages from Scripture. The Bible includes 1,800 different verses where Jesus is talking. And out of those 1,800 verses, Jesus quotes the Old Testament in 180 of them! That would be as if you quoted a Bible verse one of out every ten times you spoke!

We study Scripture because Jesus did. But we also do it because…

- Scripture shows us who Jesus is.

- Scripture shows us who we are.

# WHO IS JESUS?

In Luke 24, we read about Jesus's last time with the disciples. He told them:

> **"'Everything must be fulfilled that is written about me in the Law of Moses, the Prophets, and the Psalms.' Then he opened their minds so they could understand the Scriptures." Luke 24:44b-45**

Jesus was trying to tell the disciples that the Old Testament pointed to Him as being the Savior of the world. Suddenly, everything the disciples had been reading in the Old Testament made total sense. They connected the dots!

For all of their lives, the disciples read and listened to the Law of Moses, the Prophets, and the Psalms. But once Jesus died and rose, they understood what these books were all about. They were all about Jesus.

Luke then records the very last two things Jesus ever said to His disciples on earth. First, Jesus tells them who He is—the Messiah.

**"He [Jesus] told them, 'This is what is written: The Messiah will suffer and rise from the dead on the third day, and repentance for the forgiveness of sins will be preached in his name to all nations, beginning at Jerusalem.'"**
**Luke 24:46-47**

## WHO ARE YOU?

Finally, after Jesus explained who He is, He told the disciples who they are.

**"You are witnesses of these things. I am going to send you what my Father has promised; but stay in the city until you have been clothed with power from on high." Luke 24:48-49**

# RED ALERT!

During the time of Jesus, the Scriptures were written on scrolls—rolled-up paper. The paper was either papyrus (made from plants) or parchment (made from animal skin).

Did you catch that? Jesus told them they are witnesses. So are you. As witnesses, that means you can give evidence or proof that something is real. You can declare to the world that Jesus is real.

Jesus also told the disciples to stay in the city of Jerusalem because He had a special promise to fulfill. He was going to send them the Holy Spirit, who would give them power from on high. They were going to grow and change in wonderful ways.

You too are growing and learning new things every day. Look back at homework assignments from last year, or even two or three years ago, if you have them. Compare your artwork from then to now. Compare your handwriting. How have you improved?

Write or draw on the figure to the right to show what makes you special. For instance, maybe you can draw the figure holding a baseball, musical instrument, or paintbrush or wearing a team uniform or your favorite color.

*On Days 13 through 19, we're going to learn how Scripture tells who Jesus is and who we are.*

# DAY 3

## PAUSE TO PRAY

### A DARK AND SILENT WORLD

Once there was a toddler who got very sick, and suddenly she could no longer hear or see. For the next five years, she lived in a completely dark and silent world. She forgot how to speak. She was scared and didn't understand what was happening around her. She said she became like a seriously wounded wild animal, describing herself as a "no-person," hardly human.

Can you imagine not being able to hear, talk, or see other people? How lonely that little girl must have felt.

Her name was Helen Keller. When she was seven years old, a teacher named Anne Sullivan helped her to break the silence. Anne taught Helen to communicate by tapping her fingers on her palms. The first word she learned was "water."

Anne taught Helen to read, write, and do many things. Helen even went to college and became a successful woman who helped many people.

However, before she learned how to communicate, Helen had a tough time building friendships. She said she felt like a ship "at sea in a dense fog." But once she learned to communicate, her world opened up and the fog began to lift.

She felt connected to other people. Communication even helped her to understand herself better.

# KEYSTONE HABIT #3

God created us to communicate—with others and with Him. Therefore, prayer is Jesus's third keystone spiritual habit.

Prayer is one way to talk with Jesus whenever and wherever we want. In fact, the four Gospels mention more than 50 times that Jesus paused for prayer or to teach others how to pray. He prayed...

- When He was alone
- In public
- Before meals
- Before important decisions
- Before or after healings and other miracles
- In nature
- Overnight
- To offer thanksgiving
- In troubling times

Look at the list above and circle the times when you Pause to Pray.

Also, Jesus didn't just pray once a day. He prayed all the time. He prayed...

- First thing in the morning
- In the evening
- Consistently
- Early
- Often

Circle the times above that describe when you pray.

# TEACH ME TO PRAY

If you feel that prayer is hard, ask Jesus for help.

When the disciples wanted to learn to pray like Jesus, they asked Him to teach them. Then Jesus told them to pray like this:

> **"Our Father in heaven, hallowed be your name, your kingdom come, your will be done, on earth as it is in heaven. Give us today our daily bread. And forgive us our debts, as we also have forgiven our debtors. And lead us not into temptation, but deliver us from the evil one." Matthew 6:9-13**

Jesus also related a parable in Luke 18:1-8 that encourages us never to give up in our prayers. That's called "persistence." Go to God every day. Pray with persistence.

Without a way to talk with God, we would feel lost, scared, and alone like Helen Keller did before she learned to communicate. God gives us the gift of prayer so we don't have to feel this way.

As Philippians 4:6 says, **"Do not be anxious about anything, but in every situation, by prayer and petition, with thanksgiving, present your requests to God."**

God loves us so much that He wants to hear from us any time of the day. It is fitting that Helen Keller's first word was "water" because prayer is like water. It refreshes, it strengthens, and we need it to live.

*On Days 20 through 26, we'll learn how to Pause to Pray, just as Jesus did.*

# RED ALERT!

One of Jesus's most famous prayer times was in the Garden of Gethsemane. "Gethsemane" means "place of the oil press." Jesus felt the sins of the world pressing down on him. Just like an oil press.

# DAY 4

## STOP FOR SOLITUDE

### KEYSTONE HABIT #4

You think you have busy days? Take a look at just one day in Jesus's life.

Mark 1:21 of *The Message* says, **"Then they entered Capernaum. When the Sabbath arrived, Jesus lost no time in getting to the meeting place. He spent the day there teaching."**

He taught ALL DAY LONG. But that was only the beginning of His day. While Jesus was teaching, a man suddenly started screaming at Him. Here's how the Bible describes it:

> **"Suddenly, while still in the meeting place, he was interrupted by a man who was deeply disturbed and yelling out, 'What business do you have here with us, Jesus? Nazarene! I know what you're up to! You're the Holy One of God, and you've come to destroy us!'**

> **"Jesus shut him up: 'Quiet! Get out of him!' The afflicting spirit threw the man into spasms, protesting loudly—and got out." Mark 1:23-25 (*The Message*)**

Whew! But Jesus's day still wasn't over. The Bible says He went on to heal many sick and tormented people.

**"That evening, after the sun was down, they brought sick and evil-afflicted people to him, the whole city lined up at his door! He cured their sick bodies and tormented spirits." Mark 1:32-33 (*The Message*)**

Jesus healed an entire city of sick people! But then He did something else that we often forget about.

**"While it was still night, way before dawn, he got up and went out to a secluded spot and prayed. Simon and those with him went looking for him. They found him and said, 'Everybody's looking for you.'" Mark 1:35-37 (*The Message*)**

Even after His crazy, busy day, Jesus didn't take a break or put His feet up on a couch. He prayed. He found solitude—alone time with God.

Solitude was Jesus's fourth keystone habit.

# STOP!

Jesus stopped for solitude 39 times in the Bible. For instance:

● He stopped for solitude before He chose His 12 disciples. (Luke 6:12-13)

● He stopped for solitude after His friend, John the Baptist, was killed. (Matthew 14:11-13)

● He stopped for solitude before going to die on the cross. (Matthew 26:36)

Jesus had many reasons to stop to be alone with His Father—and so do you. For instance, here are just some of the times when you'll want to be with your Father in Heaven.

- Before a big event in your life, like a big move, a new school, or the birth of a sibling

- After something sad happens in your life

- When you have to make a decision or have a big task ahead of you

We all have crazy, busy days. But when we don't stop for solitude, we can find ourselves just hurrying from one thing to the next. So slow down. Be with God. Let Jesus enter your day.

## COLOR ME BUSY

Color in the circle that best describes how busy you are:

I'M NOT BUSY AT ALL.

SOMETIMES I AM BUSY, BUT NOT A LOT.

I OFTEN HAVE STUFF GOING ON AT NIGHT.

I HARDLY EVER HAVE A FULL DAY AT HOME.

I NEVER STOP! IT'S CRAZYTOWN AT OUR HOUSE!

*On Days 27 through 33, we will seek solitude together. When you're alone, focus on God and listen to how He calls you to live.*

# RED ALERT!

Capernaum, the town where Jesus had this crazy, busy day, is where Jesus based His ministry. It's found on the northwest shore of the Sea of Galilee. Archaeologists uncovered what they believe is Peter's house in Capernaum.

#BEINGCHALLENGEKIDS

# DAY 5

## CHOOSE CHURCH

---

### KEYSTONE HABIT #5

The Church is not the building we go to every Sunday. The Church is the people. The Church is us, just like the song says:

> I am the church! You are the church!
> We are the church together!
> All who follow Jesus,
> All around the world!
> Yes, we're the church together!
>
> The church is not a building;
> The church is not a steeple;
> The church is not a resting place;
> The church is a people.

The Bible says that God is building us—you and me—into the Church. We are the stones, and He is using us to build His temple! The Bible puts it this way:

**"God is building a home. He's using us all—irrespective of how we got here—in what he is building. He used the apostles and prophets for the foundation. Now he's using you, fitting you in brick by brick, stone**

**by stone, with Christ Jesus as the cornerstone that holds all the parts together. We see it taking shape day after day—a holy temple built by God, all of us built into it, a temple in which God is quite at home."**
**Ephesians 2:19-22 (*The Message*)**

The fifth spiritual keystone habit is to Choose Church.

# THE CORNERSTONE

Did you notice that the verse from Ephesians called Jesus "the cornerstone"? What in the world is a cornerstone?

In Bible days, buildings were often made of cut squares of stone. The cornerstone was an important stone placed at the corner of the building where two walls meet. All of the other stones lined up with the all-important cornerstone. It held the building together. It strengthened the building.

Jesus is *our* cornerstone. He holds the Church together. And we are like the other stones that are built upon the cornerstone.

# MANY TYPES OF CHURCHES—AND PEOPLE

Some church buildings are elegant and beautiful, while others are simple, made with mud bricks and a tin roof. Some churches even meet in people's living rooms. Church buildings are very different, and so are the people inside the church.

The Church includes everyone from the oldest grandma to the smallest baby. In church, you'll see hair of every color of the rainbow and all types of skin colors. People in churches speak many languages and use different kinds of musical instruments.

*We're many kinds of people,*
*With many kinds of faces,*
*All colors and ages, too*
*From all times and places.*

Although not all churches look alike, every church has two things in common—a people and a promise. Jesus promises to be with His people. As He said in Matthew 18:20 (*English Standard Version*), **"For where two or more are gathered in my name, there I am among them."**

# WE ARE THE BODY

The Bible doesn't just describe the Church as a temple. It describes the Church as a Body, and we are the many parts. **"Now you are the body of Christ and individually members of it,"** says 1 Corinthians 12:27 (*English Standard Version*).

This means some of us are like arms, some are like legs, and some are like eyes. It means we ALL have important jobs to do. Even the big toenail.

*Sometimes the church is marching;*
*Sometimes it's bravely burning,*
*Sometimes it's riding, sometimes hiding;*
*Always it's learning.*

# WE ARE THE FLOCK

The Bible also compares the Church to a flock of sheep, with Jesus as our Good Shepherd. Sheep can actually recognize the voice of their specific shepherd. So we too must listen for the voice of our Shepherd—Jesus. He calls to us every day.

Although we're one flock, we're called to welcome new people into our fold. Jesus said, **"I have other sheep that are not of this sheep pen. I must bring them also. They too will listen to my voice, and there will be one flock and one shepherd." John 10:16**

Finally, Jesus protects us, just as a shepherd does for his sheep, fighting off wolves with a staff. We need His protection because in some places of the world, it can be dangerous to meet for church. In some places, it's even illegal. But with Jesus looking out for us, we can be joyful in everything.

*On Days 34 through 40, we'll learn about ways to Choose Church.*

# RED ALERT!

Psalm 23:2a says that God "makes me lie down in green pastures." Real sheep will not lie down unless they feel completely safe and well fed. Jesus, our Good Shepherd, keeps us safe, so we can lie down in green pastures.

DAYS

6-12

OF THE 40 DAY

CHALLENGE

KEYSTONE HABIT 1:

# FORM FRIEND

# SHIPS

HAVE FUN COLORING THIS PAGE!
FIND MORE LIKE THIS AT BEINGCHALLENGE.COM/KIDS

# THE SANDS OF REDVALE

## PART 2

Aiden didn't believe a word that Emily was telling him. When she barged into his room, babbling about Redvale and Red the Fox, he was sure she was pulling his leg. He figured she was bored out of her mind and just teasing him.

But she was putting on a pretty good act.

"We gotta tell Isabella," Emily said, yanking him by the arm.

"But my baseball cards…" Aiden was sitting on his bedroom floor, just starting to organize his cards. Cleaning his room was actually kind of fun when it involved baseball cards.

"Forget your cards! This is soooo much more important! I think they need our help in Redvale!"

"Right," Aiden said. He still didn't believe her.

Ever since they had been stuck in the Covid-19 lockdown, he spent a lot of time teasing his sisters. It had almost become a sport for him. Now, Emily was just teasing him back, and he wasn't going to fall for her joke. But he still agreed to follow her, as she darted for Isabella's room. He wanted to see how the joke went over with their big sister.

When Emily told Isabella what she saw in her closet, their older sister had the strangest reaction. "I think I'm too old for that stuff," she said.

*That stuff?*" Emily shouted. "That stuff was the greatest adventure of our life!"

"I'm too old for make-believe."

"Make-believe?" Emily looked as if steam was about to come out of her ears.

Even Aiden was getting miffed. "Redvale was real!" he shouted. "You believe that, don't you?"

"I'm not so sure anymore. It seems like a dream now."

"But that's crazy!" Aiden exclaimed. "All three of us couldn't have had the exact same dream."

About seven months ago, the three of them had been whisked away to Redvale, where they got caught in a sandstorm, came face-to-face with a Cave Whale, got lost in a forest, almost got sucked into a whirlpool, and sailed across an ocean to deliver gifts to a king. For Aiden, all of that was as real as the floor beneath his feet.

"C'mon, no time to lose!" Emily shouted. She and Aiden yanked at their older sister, one on each arm.

"Cut it out, you're hurting me," Isabella complained, but at least she was moving. Aiden suddenly realized that he was acting as if he now believed Emily. If it turned out that she was just joking, he was going to be furious.

Emily's bedroom was at the end of the hallway. They dragged Isabella all the way there, and then Emily dashed to her closet on the far side of the room. She flung open the closet door, like the host of a game show making the big reveal. Then they all stared inside.

*Clothes!* They were staring at nothing but piles of clothes.

# THROUGH THE CLOSET

Isabella was almost relieved that Emily was joking. When Isabella said their earlier visit to Redvale was just a dream, that wasn't exactly true. Redvale still felt real to her, even half a year later. But she had a hard time admitting that it existed. She was almost...well, she was almost *afraid* to believe it was real.

"Em, this isn't funny," Isabella said.

"Yeah, not funny at all," added Aiden.

"But...but...Wait, don't leave! I'm not kidding. I really saw Red motioning to me from the closet!"

"I've got baseball cards to organize."

"And I've got clothes to hang up," said Isabella.

"You've got to believe me!"

"We don't have to do anything," Isabella said, heading for the door.

*"Help us!"*

Isabella stopped in her tracks. Then turned. "Who said that?"

"Not me," said Emily.

"Not me," added Aiden.

All three Perez kids stood as still as trees. They listened. They were so quiet, they could hear the tick-tock of the Mickey Mouse clock on Emily's dresser.

*"Help us!"*

The voice was faint—but real.

Isabella's heart dropped. Could it be true? A voice was coming from Emily's closet!

Isabella had been trying to forget about Redvale ever since the kids at school started teasing her. It had taken her about three months before she worked up the courage to tell her two best friends about their adventure in Redvale. But somehow other kids found out, and the teasing still hadn't stopped.

*"Emily! Aiden! Isabella! Help!"*

There it was again. A voice was definitely calling their names. Isabella couldn't ignore that. Could she? She moved directly in front of the closet and stared at the mess of clothes.

*"Follow me!"* came a second voice, this one a little louder. It still sounded far away, as if it were being carried away by the wind. Isabella saw something move

in the darkness, toward the back of the closet. Was it a person? It looked a bit like Malachi, the man who led them through Redvale. He was motioning to them.

Isabella didn't want to walk into the closet, but it was as if her feet had a mind of their own. She found herself following Emily and Aiden into the darkness.

"Whew, these stink," Aiden said, plucking a pair of dirty socks hanging on the clothes pole at the back of the closet.

"Yeah, well you—"

Emily didn't finish her sentence. A roar of wind suddenly hit them squarely in the face, followed by a blast of sand. Sand poured from the darkness, like a swarm of flying insects. Isabella staggered back several steps, but then a hand latched onto her arm and yanked her forward.

Was that Aiden again, pretending to be Sticky Hands? She couldn't see a thing with all of the swirling sand hitting her in the face, but the hand kept pulling her forward.

With the wind howling in her ears, Isabella kept trudging forward, step after step after step. She no longer felt the firm foundation of their house. She was trudging through sand, and it was getting deeper by the second.

What was she getting herself into? She wasn't sure if she could face another adventure. And yet…And yet…

She couldn't resist. She kept pressing forward.

Then, just like that, the sandstorm let up, and she saw the sun. A blazing bright sun. And blue sky. She also felt the full force of the desert heat.

As her eyes slowly came into focus, she found herself staring at a grinning red fox. Next to the fox was Malachi, a tall, bearded man wearing clothes like someone from the Bible (except for the gym shoes). All around them was desert, as far as the eye could see.

"It took you long enough," said Red the Fox.

# BACK TO CHERRYFIELD

"Hurry, hurry, no time to lose!" said Red, taking Emily by the hand. Emily staggered and nearly took a tumble because she was woozy from the trip through the closet.

"Hold on, Red," said Malachi. "Give our friends time to adjust."

The fox dropped Emily's hand, folded his arms across his chest, and tapped his right foot. "All right, time's up. You're adjusted now."

"Red," said Malachi. "Patience."

Emily was glad she was getting a chance to catch her breath. In addition to feeling dizzy, her hair was filled with sand, and she had even swallowed some of it. Malachi handed her his canteen, and she washed out her mouth.

"See, Isabella!" Emily said when she had regained her senses. "Redvale is real!"

Red glared at Isabella. "What does Emily mean by that? You don't believe in Redvale? Do you think I'm just a figment of your imagination?"

Isabella looked horrified. "I didn't say that."

Emily pounced. "Yes, you did!"

Red and Emily both started to say something not very polite when Malachi put up a hand to cut them off. "Emily, someone in your world once wrote, 'Love one another with brotherly affection. Outdo one another in showing honor.' I think that also means showing *sisterly* affection. Don't be so hard on Isabella."

Emily turned red with embarrassment. She hated being corrected in front of her brother and sister. But at least Red was on her side.

"I think you were right to get mad," the fox whispered to her.

After the canteen had been passed around a second time, Malachi removed his gym shoes and poured out a stream of sand.

"I see you're still wearing the same old gym shoes," Aiden said.

"This is a new model," he said. "Better insoles."

"Okay, okay, NOW can we tell them what's been happening in Redvale?" Red asked, hopping around impatiently.

"I think it's better if we *show them* what's been happening," said Malachi. He turned, jammed his wooden staff into the sand, and began hiking up the dune. The others followed, with Red muttering to himself every step of the way.

Just over the dune, they saw a familiar sight—a wonder to behold. It was the small village of Cherryfield, the starting point for their first adventure. The houses were made of stone, with red shutters on the windows and thatch roofs. Some of the roofs and doors were also red.

But something was wrong with this picture.

Emily shaded her eyes from the glaring sun and saw the problem. Several of the houses had collapsed into a heap. Others had holes in their walls and roofs.

"What happened?" she asked. "A windstorm?"

"Worse," said Red.

"You mean the Destroyers?" asked Isabella.

"Yes! The Destroyers are turning everything to sand!" Red exclaimed.

As they entered the village, Emily saw what he meant. One house had completely collapsed into a mound of sand.

Aiden pointed at a house with a gaping hole in the roof. "Was that because of the Destroyers too?"

"Part of the roof turned to sand and caved in," said Malachi.

"And that door?" Emily said. "It turned to sand?" She pointed at half a door. The top half had crumbled away.

"That's right," said Red. "It's terrible."

At the end of the main road was a large building—the very place where they had first witnessed the terrible power of the Destroyers during their last visit. At least it was still standing.

"Where is everyone?" Isabella asked. Emily had been wondering the same thing. The village was empty.

"They're all inside. Waiting for you," said Red.

"Us?" Emily was nervous but strangely excited by those words.

"Follow me," said Malachi.

And so they did.

# THE MISSION

As they strode through the front door, they found a packed room. All eyes turned in their direction.

Aiden looked up to the ceiling and saw three red banners hanging by the wooden rafters, each with one of their names splashed across it—just like before. It made him feel very important.

At the front of the room were three ordinary chairs, but off to the side was a much larger, fancier chair—almost like a throne. He made a beeline for it because why sit on a regular chair when you can sit on a throne?

"Wait, Aiden, don't…"

Malachi didn't get the words out fast enough.

*WHOOOOMP!*

When Aiden sat on the throne, it collapsed under him, like a folding chair. Red, Emily, and Isabella started giggling, although no one else in the room laughed. Aiden felt the sting of embarrassment.

"I was trying to tell you," Malachi said, helping him to his feet. "Part of that throne turned to sand. It couldn't hold your weight."

Still red in the face, Aiden took a seat between his sisters, who couldn't contain their grins. Aiden tried to act dignified as Malachi explained what was happening in Redvale.

"The Destroyers have released tiny creatures into our world—too small for us to see. These creatures—sandspinners they're called—are transforming everything around us into sand."

"Can they be stopped?" Aiden asked.

"We think so. We think *you three* can stop them."

"Oh, I don't know about that..." Isabella started to say, but Emily shushed her.

"Tell us what we can do," Emily said.

"To stop them, we must find the Sand Sovereign and his Sand Castle."

"Sand Castle?" Aiden said. "You mean like the sand castles we build on the beaches when we go to Fort Myers?"

"Kind of. However, this Sand Castle is as a big as any stone castle you'll find in England."

"Cool."

"Not so cool," said Red. "We believe the sandspinners are being sent out from the Sand Castle to destroy our world."

"So how do we stop the sandspinners once we get there?" Isabella asked.

"I'm not exactly sure yet," said Malachi. "But the king says we can find the answer in this box."

Malachi pointed at a red, metal box—about four feet wide and three feet high. It was set to the side, just beyond the broken throne. The last time they were in Redvale, their job was to deliver three treasure chests to the king. This time, they were dealing with a single red box.

"Let's open it!" said Aiden, kneeling down and trying to unlatch the lid. It was locked. When he tried to move the box, he could barely budge it. Whatever was inside must weigh a ton.

"What's in it?" Emily asked.

"I wish I knew what's inside the Sand Box," said Malachi.

"The Sand Box?" said Isabella.

"I call it the Sand Box because it contains the secret to survival in a world where everything is changing to sand."

Malachi pulled a large, golden key from his right sleeve and continued. "To open the Sand Box, we need five keys. This is the first key, but we must find four more. Here, give it a try, Aiden."

"Sure thing." Taking the key from Malachi, Aiden noticed that its handle had the picture of three people etched into it. The three people sort of resembled Emily, Isabella, and himself.

However, when Aiden tried to insert the key in the first hole, it didn't fit. He tried the other four keyholes, but still no success. Once again, he felt embarrassed. The eyes of the entire room were on him.

"Here, let me try," Emily said, wrestling the key out of Aiden's hand. But when she put the key into the holes, it still wouldn't fit.

"It's not so easy is it, smartypants?" Aiden said. Now, it was Emily's turn to blush with embarrassment.

"Would you like to give it a try?" Malachi asked Isabella.

"Nah, I'm okay."

"Just try it," Malachi insisted, so Isabella gave a heavy sigh, took the key from Emily, and approached the box. But, once again, the key wouldn't fit.

"Told you," she muttered. "Why did you even ask me to try?"

"To make a point," Malachi said. "None of you can do this on your own. Now, I want all of you to put your hands on the key at the same time."

"Huh?" said Aiden.

"Just do what he says," grumbled Emily.

Aiden put his hand on Isabella's, and Emily put her hand on Aiden's—and together they inserted the key. This time, it fit smoothly into the first hole, and they turned it with a CLICK.

"I don't get it," Aiden said. "None of us could get the key to fit, and now it suddenly works?"

"This is the Friendship Key," Malachi said. "One of the keys to life are friends and family. And yes, brothers and sisters are friends too, even if you don't always treat each other that way. God calls you to love one another, even when you're getting on each other's nerves. You need each other. That's why the key wouldn't work when you tried to insert it by yourself. You must do it together."

"But now we need to find the other four keys," said Red. "So, what are we waiting for? Let's get going!"

"How will we know where to find the keys—or the Sand Castle?" asked Aiden.

"Follow the flags," came a voice from the crowd. One of the Cherryfield residents carried a flag on a long pole to the front of the room. The flag displayed the picture of two large keys and an upside-down cross.

"I've seen that picture somewhere before," Isabella said.

"This is the flag of Peter, Jesus's main disciple," the man explained. "After Peter confessed that Jesus is Lord, Jesus gave him the keys of the kingdom of heaven. This was the beginning of the Church, and it's why the flag shows two keys."

"But why does it also show an upside-down cross?" Aiden asked.

"When Peter was killed, people believe he was crucified," Malachi pointed out. "However, Peter didn't think he was worthy of being crucified in the *exact* same way as Jesus. So he asked to be put on the cross upside down."

"There are eleven more flags out there in the desert, each one showing the symbol of another disciple—Jesus's closest friends," Red explained. "These flags will lead us to the castle."

"We'll also find the other four keys along the way," added Malachi.

"I'm surprised the Destroyers haven't destroyed all of the flags," said Aiden.

"Oh, they've tried," said Malachi. "But the king has put his protection on them. Time is running out. We must leave immediately."

Aiden leaped to his feet, fired up to go.

"When we reach the Sand Castle, all we need to do is defeat the Sand Dragon and the sandspinners before everything in Redvale turns to sand," Malachi added. *Hold on a second*, Aiden thought. *What's this about a dragon?* He sat back down.

# INTO THE WILDERNESS

"Sand Dragon?" Isabella exclaimed. "You didn't say anything about a dragon!"

"Oh, did I forget to mention that?" said Malachi. "Nothing to worry about. The Sand Sovereign's castle is protected by a Sand Dragon. But we'll be prepared by the time we fight the creature."

Malachi talked as if it would be as easy as a walk in the park.

"Do we have weapons to fight this monster?" asked Aiden. "A laser? Or maybe a phaser? Or a sonic screwdriver? Or a lightsaber? Or a...?"

"Your weapon is your love for one another," Malachi said.

Isabella stared at her feet and chewed her lip. Over the past month, the three of them hadn't been very good at showing love to one another. Besides, she agreed with Aiden. Couldn't they be given a lightsaber instead?

"Our weapon is love?" Aiden exclaimed. "That's the craziest thing I ever heard. Love isn't a weapon!"

"You'll see the truth for yourself along the way," Malachi said, motioning toward the front door. "The village has prepared our supplies and our transportation. So let's move out!"

Two villagers—a man and woman—stood on either side of the large front doors. When Malachi nodded, they pulled open the doors and light gushed in. Standing in the doorway, silhouetted by the sun, was a camel.

"I can't believe it!" shouted Emily, sprinting for the open door, followed close behind by Aiden. Even Isabella burst into a big grin when she saw who was standing in the doorway. It was Melchior the camel.

The sight of their old friend gave Isabella a touch of hope, like feeling a cool breeze on a hot afternoon.

## TO BE CONTINUED ON PAGE 84.

# DAY 6

## WIRED FOR RELATIONSHIPS

---

### FRIENDS ON THE BRAIN

When we connect with people, our brains light up. Scientists found that when we share deep secrets with others—our fears and dreams—part of the brain lights up like a Christmas tree. It also causes our brain to send out a certain chemical that makes us feel good.

In other words, God created our brains to enjoy being with other people.

Many of the great heroes of the Bible had good friends. Moses's greatest friend was also his brother—Aaron. David's BFF was Jonathan. Elijah hung out with his good buddy, Elisha. (They even had similar names!) Paul had Barnabas and Silas.

Jesus also had different circles of friends—the 3, the 12, the 72, and the 500. But before we talk about those, let's start with the Trinity.

### THREE IN ONE

Jesus has had a relationship with God the Father and God the Holy Spirit since before creation. This mystery is called the Trinity, which means there are 3 persons, but 1 God.

In the beginning, God created us to be in relationship. In fact, one of the first things that God said to Adam in the Garden of Eden was: **"It is not good for the man to be alone." Genesis 2:18**

Jesus didn't need others to complete His mission, but He still chose to have close friendships. He knew we were created to be with others. Jesus didn't have favorites, but there were special groups in His life, beginning with...

# THE 3

Peter, James, and John were the closest disciples to Jesus. Sometimes, Jesus went off with these three for a special purpose. For instance, He took them to pray in the Garden of Gethsemane before He died. He also took them along when He healed Jairus's daughter.

Mark 9:2 says, **"After six days Jesus took Peter, James and John with him and led them up a high mountain, where they were all alone. There he was transfigured before them."** The transfiguration was when Jesus's clothes shone as bright as lightning, and Moses and Elijah appeared with Him.

Jesus didn't choose Peter, James, and John because they were the "best" of the disciples. They were sinful like everyone else. In fact, all three had pretty hot tempers. Jesus chose them because He had special missions for them.

We too have a small number of people with whom we're closest to, such as our family.

## THE 12

Jesus also chose 12 disciples, who spent three years following Him across the land. After Jesus died and rose again, He sent these disciples out to preach to the farthest reaches of the world.

Again, Jesus didn't choose the 12 because they were the "cool ones." He chose them for a certain job—to carry His message and reach the lost. As Mark 3:14 says, Jesus **"appointed twelve that they might be with him and that he might send them out to preach."**

In our lives, we have people like the 12—cousins, aunts, uncles, or kids we play with or go to school with.

## RED ALERT!

When Jesus sent out the 12 disciples in Mark 6:8-11, He said to bring nothing but a staff. A staff was used for protection against robbers, snakes, and other creatures. Travelers also used staffs to keep their balance on mountain paths.

# THE 72

In addition to the 3 and the 12, Jesus had 72 people who followed Him. We don't know all of their names, but Luke 10:1 says the Lord **"sent them two by two ahead of him to every town and place where he was about to go."** Jesus sent them two-by-two because He knew the importance of having a friend by your side.

Your "72" could be a sports team, your class, or another large group.

# THE 500

Paul writes in 1 Corinthians 15:6 that after the resurrection, Jesus **"appeared to more than 500 of the brothers and sisters at the same time."** In addition, there were times in Jesus's life when he gathered with large groups of even more than 500 to preach or heal.

We too belong to big groups. It could be your neighborhood, church, or school. Or maybe it's being part of an event like walking in a 5K, going to a concert, or attending a state fair.

You probably won't know everybody's name in a group of 500, but you're still part of the group. You have something in common with them. Big groups can accomplish big things, especially when everyone is working toward the same goal.

So Jesus had groups of 3, 12, 72, and 500. But in each one, God was in the center.

Think of the people in your life. Who are your 3, 12, 72, and 500? They don't have to be exact numbers. For example, your 3 are the closest people in your life. They could be your mom and dad, so in that case you'd put two names down. Or you might want to add your brothers and sisters, so your number could be more than three.

## YOUR 3
**(FAMILY, PARENTS, GUARDIANS)**

_____

_____

## YOUR 12
**(EXTENDED FAMILY, BEST FRIENDS, SIBLINGS)**

_____

_____

_____

## YOUR 72
**(CLASS, TEAM, LARGE GROUP)**

_____

_____

_____

## YOUR 500
**(CHURCH, NEIGHBORHOOD, SCHOOL)**

_____

_____

_____

# TARGET PRACTICE

As we begin this week on friendships, answer these two questions by coloring the ring of the target that connects to your answer.

## DO YOU HAVE FRIENDSHIPS THAT POINT YOU TO JESUS?

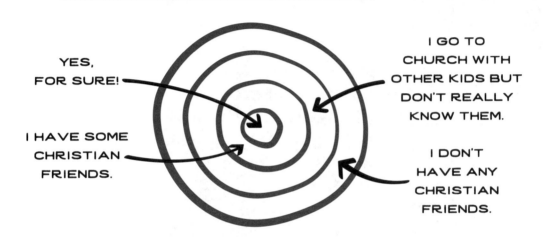

YES, FOR SURE!

I HAVE SOME CHRISTIAN FRIENDS.

I GO TO CHURCH WITH OTHER KIDS BUT DON'T REALLY KNOW THEM.

I DON'T HAVE ANY CHRISTIAN FRIENDS.

## ARE YOU POINTING YOUR FRIENDS AND FAMILY TO JESUS?

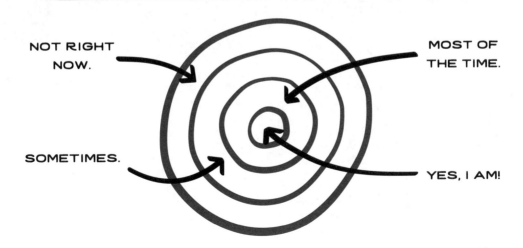

NOT RIGHT NOW.

SOMETIMES.

MOST OF THE TIME.

YES, I AM!

# DAY 7

## THE POWER OF THE TEAM

### THE BUNDLE OF STICKS

*Once there was a father, whose sons and daughters constantly bickered with each other. On the drive to school, they fought about who got to sit in the front seat. After school, they squabbled about who had to take out the garbage. In the evening, they argued about what to watch on TV.*

*Finally, the father decided he had to do something to show his children that they needed to work and play together. So he brought them a thick bundle of sticks and asked each one to try to break it in half.*

*The kids argued about who would be able to break the sticks. But as each one took their turn, not one could bust an entire bundle of sticks.*

*Next, the father took single sticks from the bundle and handed one to each of them.*

*"Now break it," he said.*

*SNAP!*

*Snapping a single stick was a piece of cake.*

*"Don't you see,"* said the father. *"When you stick together, you are strong and cannot be broken. But when you fight among yourselves, you are divided and weak. You become like single sticks, which can be broken easily. In unity is strength."*

This is a modern version of a very old fable, once told by a Greek slave and storyteller named Aesop. He most likely lived between 620 and 560 B.C., but his story still rings true today. When we are united in a group, we are stronger.

## BIRDS OF A FEATHER STICK TOGETHER

Being part of a group can keep you safe and help you learn certain things. We see this throughout nature. How do you think the animals in this picture stay safe? The answers are on page 60.

# TREES COMPANY

Another example from nature is the Aspen tree. What makes this tree different from other trees is that most of them grow in groups. The Aspen tree creates new trees through "root suckers." These are new stems in its root system that grow up through the soil and become new Aspen trees.

Above the ground, Aspens look like separate trees. But if you could peek underground, you'd see one giant cobweb of roots, all connecting them. They are one organism, even though they are many trees.

Because the trees are all connected, they help each other. The taller trees soak up sunlight, while smaller ones pull nutrients from the soil and share them with the other trees. The trees need the group to stay alive.

Like Aspen trees, we too are part of different groups, or communities—our 3, 12, 72, and 500 communities. In each of these groups, you have "roots" or relationships with other people.

These connections shape you for good or bad. (After all, some groups use their power for evil.) Christians build strong connections by sharing, supporting, and praying for one another. These are the unseen roots that bind us together.

> **"Even so the body is not made up of one part but of many."**
> **1 Corinthians 12:14**

# THE THIRD STRAND

> **"By yourself you're unprotected. With a friend you can face the worst. Can you round up a third? A three-stranded rope isn't easily snapped."**
> **Ecclesiastes 4:12 (The Message)**

As Christians, we all have a third strand that is unbreakable. That third strand is Jesus. Sometimes in your life, you will feel alone and lost. But even when other people let you down, you're never alone. You will never be broken when Jesus is with you.

> **"...for the power of the wicked will be broken, but the Lord upholds the righteous." Psalm 37:17**

# CHALLENGE

Get five toothpicks. Tape them together and try to break them in half.

Next, take off the tape and then try to break the toothpicks one by one.

Talk about what this teaches you about the strength of groups. Also, think about your class at school or a team you're on. Can you remember everyone's name?

What are people's different roles in the group?

Write your team name or class below and fill in the blanks.

I am a part of _____ class or team.

We have _____ kids in our class or on our team.

I like being in this group because _____

_____

_____

I can show Jesus's love to this group by _____

_____

_____

_____

**Answer Key**
1. Birds migrate together so they all wind up in the right place.
2. Fish stay together to fool enemies into thinking they are one big fish and are harder to attack.
3. Lions hunt together to share food. Not everyone will catch dinner, so they must share.
4. Penguins huddle together to increase their body temperature and keep warm.

# RED ALERT!

1 Corinthians 15:6 says Jesus appeared to more than 500 people after His resurrection. This was proof that people weren't just seeing things. Five hundred people wouldn't see the same thing— unless it was real!

#BEINGCHALLENGEKIDS

# DAY 8

## YOUR FRIENDS MAKE A DIFFERENCE

### MIXING IT UP

Over 3,000 years ago, even before Jesus was born, people did an experiment that changed the world. They mixed together two metals—tin and copper—to create a brand new material called bronze.

Bronze became the strongest material known to humans. It was used to make weapons, tools, chariots, and even jewelry. Bronze was such an important invention that people called the entire time period "The Bronze Age."

Set a timer for one minute and see how many new words you can create out of various letters in the phrase "The Bronze Age." We've started you out with two words.

## THE BRONZE AGE

ON _____    _____    _____

TEA _____

_____    _____    _____

_____    _____    _____

Tin and copper make bronze, and you just made all kinds of words out of the phrase "The Bronze Age." In the same way, you can create something new and beautiful when you mix different people together in a group. Each person brings special talents, personalities, and gifts to the group.

That's why groups of good friends are so important. They can do amazing things to help one other, like the four men in the Bible who helped their paralyzed friend.

## AMAZING FRIENDS!

Jesus attracted huge crowds. So, when He came to a house one day, it became packed with people who wanted to be healed or hear Him teach.

Four men brought their paralyzed friend to be healed, but the house was so crowded that they couldn't get through the door. But where there's a will, there's a way. These friends dug through the roof! Then they lowered their paralyzed friend on a mat through the hole. Here's what happened next.

> **"When Jesus saw their faith, he said to the paralyzed man, 'Son, your sins are forgiven.'**

> **"Now some teachers of the law were sitting there, thinking to themselves, 'Why does this fellow talk like that? He's blaspheming! Who can forgive sins but God alone?'**

> **"Immediately Jesus knew in his spirit that this was what they were thinking in their hearts, and he said to them, 'Why are you thinking these things? Which is easier: to say to this paralyzed man, 'Your sins are forgiven,' or to say, 'Get up, take your mat and walk'? But I want you to know that the**

Son of Man has authority on earth to forgive sins.' **So he said to the man, 'I tell you, get up, take your mat and go home.' He got up, took his mat and walked out in full view of them all. This amazed everyone and they praised God, saying, 'We have never seen anything like this!'"**
**Mark 2:5-12**

Nothing could stop these men from helping their friend—not even a roof. But what drove these men to go to such lengths? To find out, fill in the blank below:

When Jesus saw their _____ , he said to the paralyzed man, **"Son, your sins are forgiven."**

# AMAZING FAITH!

If it hadn't been for the four friends, the paralyzed man never would have met Jesus face-to-face and been healed. Jesus saw the amazing faith of these four friends.

It makes a big difference who your friends are. They can help us—or hurt us. For example, research studies show that when people lose a lot of weight, their friends are more likely to lose weight too. The same with gaining weight.

Who we hang out with also affects us *spiritually*. Like the four friends who helped their paralyzed friend, our friends and family can help us see and follow Jesus. In fact, your parents may be a big reason why you're reading this book.

As it says in Proverbs 13:20, **"Whoever walks with the wise becomes wise, but the companion of fools will suffer harm."** (*English Standard Version*)

# PICK UP YOUR MAT

Jesus knew the paralyzed man wanted desperately to walk. But first, Jesus gave the man something he needed even more: forgiveness of sins. Sometimes, the miracles we *can't* see are even more amazing than the ones we can see. We're all sinners. We all mess up. We cannot lift ourselves out of our sins on our own strength, just as the paralyzed man couldn't stand up on his own. But Jesus offers us forgiveness of sins and eternal life. He raises us up out of our life of sin. He frees us and strengthens us.

Jesus can make us as strong as bronze because in His eyes we are as precious as gold.

# CHALLENGE

In one of the boxes below, write or draw a wish or big dream of yours. For example: learn to ride a bike, play an instrument, visit another country, try a new sport, take a painting class, learn to sew, bake a cake by yourself, etc. Next, write or draw who will help you reach this dream.

| MY BIG DREAM | WHO WILL HELP? |
|---|---|
|  |  |

# DAY 9

## FORM FRIENDSHIPS

## YOU CAN MAKE A DIFFERENCE TOO

### THE FUTURE YOU

Imagine that you're in a time machine, and it's zooming toward the future. Suddenly, the time machine loses control and crashes in your own backyard. You survive with a few scratches. So you climb out of the machine and knock on your back door. Who should answer? Your future self!

If you met your future self, what kind of job do you think you'd be doing as an adult? Draw your "future self" on the figure of the person to the right.

How would your future job help people in your community? Some jobs are more obviously "helping jobs" than others, such as a doctor, teacher, or firefighter. But what if you want to be a ballerina or filmmaker? Think about how jobs like these can help people too.

You may not be sure what you want to do when you get older, but be sure of this. God absolutely has plans for you. He created you for a purpose. Also, no matter what job you pick, there's one thing everyone is invited to do—to follow Jesus and love others.

> **"For I know the plans I have for you," declares the Lord, "plans to prosper you and not to harm you, plans to give you hope and a future." Jeremiah 29:11**

# NOBLE CAUSES

Yesterday, you learned how other people and groups can make a big difference in your life. But today we're going to think about how you can help your friends and community.

## THE 3—FAMILY, PARENTS, GUARDIANS

Sometimes, it's hardest to show love to the people closest to us. We know what bugs each other. We take each other for granted. Therefore, it can be hard to be a humble helper. However, you can help your family by:

● Respecting their things and space

● Forgiving each other when we mess up

● Serving one another

"He has shown you, O mortal, what is good. And what does the Lord require of you? To act justly and to love mercy and to walk humbly with your God." Micah 6:8

## THE 12—EXTENDED FAMILY, BEST FRIENDS, SIBLINGS

You can help your close friends by using your talents for others, not just for yourself. If math comes easily for you, help out a buddy who struggles with it. Let your sibling have first choice of the brownies. Help your cousin with yardwork and make it fun!

"And do not forget to do good and to share with others, for with such sacrifices God is pleased." Hebrews 13:16

## THE 72—CLASS, TEAM, OR LARGE GROUP

Make sure everyone is treated fairly in your class, team, or club. Maybe you know kids who are picked on. Or maybe you know someone who doesn't have much money to buy fancy clothes or shoes. Stick up for them. Don't join in when others laugh or whisper mean things about them. When people are rejected, ask to be their partner. Sit by them. A friendly smile can brighten someone's day.

"Defend the weak and the fatherless; uphold the cause of the poor and the oppressed." Psalm 82:3

## THE 500—CHURCH OR NEIGHBORHOOD

Proclaiming the Gospel to all the world is a noble cause, a great mission. Reaching the world may seem impossible for one person, but you're not just one person. You're connected to a big community through Jesus's love.

Christians are linked together by the Good News, just like the interconnected roots of Aspen trees we learned about on Day 7. The Christian family is huge, with brothers and sisters all over the world. We can unite to reach the entire world with the message of Jesus.

When we join with our church, neighborhood, or school, we can do greater things than we can do alone. But the only reason we are able to help and love others is because God first loved us. Before you were born, Jesus loved you. He loves us yesterday, today, and tomorrow.

In fact, if we travel to the future, He'll still be there with open arms.

# CHALLENGE

Pick one of the challenges from the list below.

- **Use your words to lift up someone in your group of 3—family, parents, or guardians.** Encourage them and tell them how special they are to you. You probably live with them, so think about a special way you can bless them today with a gift, favor, or hug.

- **Bring a treat or snack to your group of 12—siblings, best friends, or extended family.** The treat doesn't have to be food. Attach a note inviting them to your church or include a Bible verse.

- **Serve your "72" today—your team, class, or club.** Wear a shirt that supports your team or club. Pray for your 72. Brainstorm a way to share Jesus's love with them.

- **Show support for your "500"—your neighborhood, church, or school.** Make a sign advertising your church, create a free lemonade stand in your neighborhood, or raise money for your school.

# DAY 10

## FRIENDS IN A DIGITAL AGE

---

### THE VIRTUAL DOG

Every birthday, Austin begged his parents for a dog. He put "dog" at the top of every Christmas list. He prayed for a dog regularly. He even checked out books about dogs and left them around the house to give his parents a hint.

One day, Austin discovered an app on his phone that allowed him to own a virtual dog. He could name this pet and give him food and water. He also could pick out a collar, take him on a walk, play catch with him, and make sure he got enough rest.

But there was a problem. His virtual dog didn't take away his longing for a real dog.

"But this is better than a real dog," Austin's mother said. "You don't have to walk him outside if the weather is bad. You don't have to pick up after his messes. And if you don't want to hear his barking, turn off your phone."

"I know it's *easier* to have a virtual pet," Austin said. "But I'm willing to put up with the problems if I could have a real dog right here with me."

Austin is like a lot of us. He knows it's harder to have a real pet, but he thinks a real dog is worth the trouble. This lesson doesn't just apply to pets. Doing something in real life, even if it's harder, is more rewarding than doing something amazing in a virtual world. After all, would you rather hit a home run in a real World Series or hit a home run on a video game?

# NOT QUITE THE SAME

Below are some examples of things we can do on our screens today. Check the boxes of the things you've done on your phone, computer, iPad, or other device.

☐ Build a virtual ice cream cone

☐ Have a virtual pet

☐ Go on a virtual safari

☐ Dig up a virtual fort

☐ Take a selfie and give yourself a makeover

☐ Use Google Earth to explore the world

☐ Go shopping at a virtual store

☐ Play a virtual sport, such as football, baseball, or soccer

☐ Go virtual go-karting

☐ Fill in the blank for something else you did virtually:

These things are fun! There's nothing wrong with playing games on your computer, as long as you have healthy limits. (Hint: 15 hours a day is NOT a healthy limit.) But as fun as these things are, it's way more exciting to do them in real life.

Now, check off all of the things you have done in real life.

- [ ] Went to an ice cream shop
- [ ] Have a real pet
- [ ] Went on a safari
- [ ] Made a fort
- [ ] Gave yourself a makeover with a friend

- [ ] Traveled with your family to another country
- [ ] Went shopping with family or friends at a mall
- [ ] Played a sport, such as football, baseball, or soccer
- [ ] Went go-karting

Screen time can be great, but it shouldn't replace Real Time.

# WORTH THE MESS

Taking care of a real dog is messy. So are human relationships.

Some people think it's easier to relate to other kids through messaging, social media, or gaming because it's less trouble. Some people prefer to watch other kids' videos than talk with them in person. Some kids will even talk to people through online games, but they never talk to the kids on their soccer team!

Even though real relationships are messy and hard, the Bible says they're worth it. As Proverbs 17:17 says, **"Friends love through all kinds of weather, and families stick together in all kinds of trouble."** (*The Message*)

Jesus's disciples were far from perfect. They got angry at each other and were prideful and sometimes jealous. For example, the other disciples probably weren't too thrilled when James and John asked Jesus if they could sit in the seats of honor to the right and left of Him in glory (Mark 10:35-45).

But even with all of their problems, Jesus never gave up on His disciples. Even when Peter denied Jesus before the crucifixion, He kept loving him. His disciples were worth the mess.

Jesus is your friend, even though you're far from perfect. He even took the punishment for your sins. But you know what? He thinks you're worth it. Because you are.

## CHALLENGE

Take a break from your normal screen time today. Instead, hang out with friends or family face-to-face.

## RED ALERT!

Joseph of Arimathea was a brave friend of Jesus. When Jesus was crucified, Joseph asked Pilate for His body. Because Joseph was not a family member of Jesus, he risked his life by making this request. He was a true friend.

# DAY 11

## FORM FRIENDSHIPS

# BETTER TOGETHER

## FLYING SOLO

When a baby horse (a "foal") is born, it takes about 55 minutes for it to stand and about 90 minutes before it can walk and run. For newborn human babies, it takes over a year before they can stand and walk. Why so long?

Some believe it's because God created us to be so complex. It takes longer for complicated things to grow and develop.

As we get older, we learn to do more and more on our own. Circle all of the things you can do on your own without help from adults.

- Set my own alarm or get up on my own
- Get dressed
- Brush my teeth
- Pack my own lunch
- Clean up my room
- Choose what I want to watch on TV

- Have my own phone/device
- Play an organized sport
- Set my own bedtime
- Ride a bike to a friend's house alone
- Have a sleepover
- Make my own breakfast

- Do my own laundry
- Earn my own money
- Write my own name
- Do my homework
- Pick out my own clothes
- Tie my shoes
- Buy things with my own money

The things you are able to do on your own depend on how old you are. By the time you're a teenager, you'll probably be able to do most of these things. Now, check out this new list. Circle all of the things you can do on your own with no help from adults.

- Drive my own car

- Own my own apartment or house

- Do my own grocery shopping

- Schedule my doctor appointments

- Make my own money

- Take care of myself when I'm sick

- Choose my own church or place of worship

- Pay my own cell phone bill

- Book my own vacations

- Own and care for a pet

The things on this list are mostly things that adults do. But someday most of you will be doing these things without the help of your parents.

## PEOPLE NEED PEOPLE

Growing up is a gift from God. Every year, you see yourself getting taller and smarter. God gives parents the job of teaching and helping their children do things on their own.

But just because it's important to learn to do things on our own doesn't mean we don't need people. Movies, advertisements, and books often send the message that we don't need anyone else to be happy.

They say we make our own happiness when…

- We get the things we want.

- We go to the places we want.

- We eat what we want.

- We wear what we want.

- We do what we want.

The idea that we can go it alone is not the truth. We need people. Every single activity on the adult list cannot be done alone. Look at that list again. Then choose one of the activities and name all of the people needed to help you with it.

ACTIVITY: _____

WHO WE NEED: _____

_____

_____

# HIS POWER MADE PERFECT

It's NOT a sign of weakness to depend on others. We're better together because we all bring different gifts. Also, we're better with God because He strengthens us and guides us.

Therefore, Jesus invites us to give up trying to do everything on our own. Let His grace take over! 2 Corinthians 12:9 says, **"My grace is sufficient for you, for**

**my power is made perfect in weakness."** Then verse 10 adds, **"For when I am weak, then I am strong."**

It takes a strong person to admit when they need help from others. And it takes a strong person to admit they need God.

> **"And my God will meet all your needs according to the riches of his glory in Christ Jesus." Philippians 4:19**

# CHALLENGE

Let's do some wishing and dreaming for your life. What is one thing on the first list of activities that you haven't learned yet—something you can work on this week? Whose help do you need to accomplish that goal? Write your answer in the thought bubble below.

Finally, take time to thank your mom, dad, guardian, teacher, or siblings for their help in teaching you how to do so many of those things on the list.

# DAY 12

## COMMIT TO ONE

---

### TAKING UP THE MANTLE

Don't confuse Elijah with Elisha. They're two different people. In fact, Elijah was Elisha's teacher.

One day, the prophet Elijah called on Elisha to follow him, and he did it in a rather unusual way. He simply strode up to Elisha while the young man was working in the field. Then he tossed his cloak over Elisha's shoulders (1 Kings 19:19-21). From that day on, Elisha followed him.

Later, when Elijah went up to heaven in a chariot of fire, he left behind that same cloak. Elisha picked up the cloak (or "mantle") because his teacher, the prophet, was gone. By picking up the cloak, he showed that he was ready to take on the task of prophet.

Elisha knew that to carry on Elijah's mission, he had to learn from the older man. To put it another way, Elisha was "accountable" to Elijah. Being accountable means checking your actions with another person. It's when you have a person in your life who knows you well, knows your goals, and can help you grow.

We all need an Elijah in our life.

# AWESOME ACCOUNTABILITY

Accountability is a gift from God. You are accountable to your parents, teachers, sitters, older siblings, or any guardian over you. Even Jesus was accountable to others! Jesus was perfect, so He didn't need to be accountable to the people around Him. But He still chose to let others into His life.

Jesus was accountable to God the Father. **"For I have come down from heaven not to do my will but to do the will of him who sent me,"** He said in John 6:38.

Jesus was also accountable to people around Him. He surrounded Himself with 12 disciples because He knew He would need a group to carry the Good News to the world. In Matthew 4:19, Jesus said, **"Come, follow me, and I will send you out to fish for people."**

# CAN YOU HEAR ME NOW?

God designed us to need others and be accountable to them. But the world often sends us a different message.

# RED ALERT!

**Before Elijah left the world, Elisha asked him for "a double portion of your spirit." Elisha was like a son to Elijah. In ancient Israel, when a father died, his oldest son received a double portion of land. But Elisha asked for something far more important than land.**

Look at the text messages on the four phones below. Each text contains a message that the world sends to us over and over. In the blank space after each text message, write down the Bible verse that is the best response to that message. (You don't need to write down the entire verse—just the book of the Bible, plus chapter and verse.) For your answers, choose from the four Bible verses below. The Answer Key is on the next page.

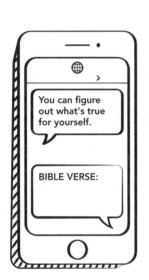

### JOHN 8:36
*So if the Son sets you free, you will be free indeed.*
Doing whatever we want, whenever we want, and however we want doesn't make us free. Jesus sets us free.

### ROMANS 12:1
*Therefore, I urge you, brothers and sisters, in view of God's mercy, to offer your bodies as a living sacrifice, holy and pleasing to God—this is your true and proper worship.*
We belong to God. We give our whole lives to Jesus, knowing He will care for us.

### PSALM 25:5
*Guide me in your truth and teach me, for you are God my Savior, and my hope is in you all day long.*
We are not left to figure out what is true for ourselves. God will help us.

### JOHN 14:24
*Anyone who does not love me will not obey my teaching. These words you hear are not my own; they belong to the Father who sent me.*
God decides what is right and wrong.

# CHALLENGE

Ask an adult or guardian to help you work through all of the challenges in this book. It's not easy learning new habits, so an accountability person can help you.

## ACCOUNTABILITY PARTNER AGREEMENT

I, _____ , agree that I will help

_____ stay accountable to these challenges.

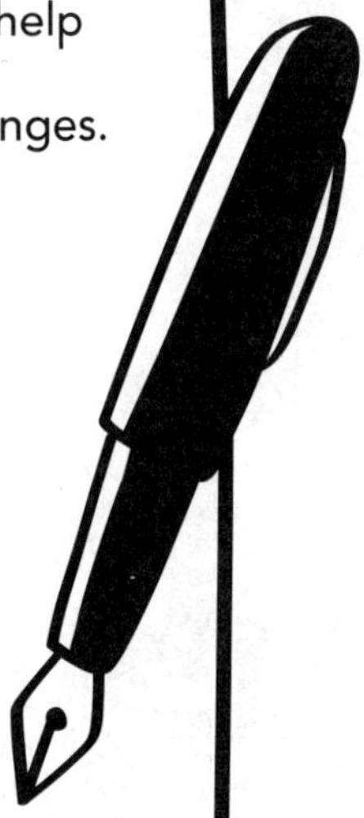

**I WILL:**

- Ask them how they're doing
- Check on them every day
- Pray for them
- Encourage them

**SIGNED:**

_____
(Me)

_____
(Accountability Partner)

**Answer Key**
You can figure out what is true for yourself. (Psalm 25:5)
You should be free to live as you choose as long as you don't hurt anyone. (John 8:36)
No one has the right to tell anyone else what is right or wrong for them. (John 14:24)
You should never sacrifice (give up) what makes you happy. (Romans 12:1)

DAYS
**13-19**
OF THE 40 DAY
CHALLENGE

## KEYSTONE HABIT 2:

# STUD
# SCRIP

Y

TURE

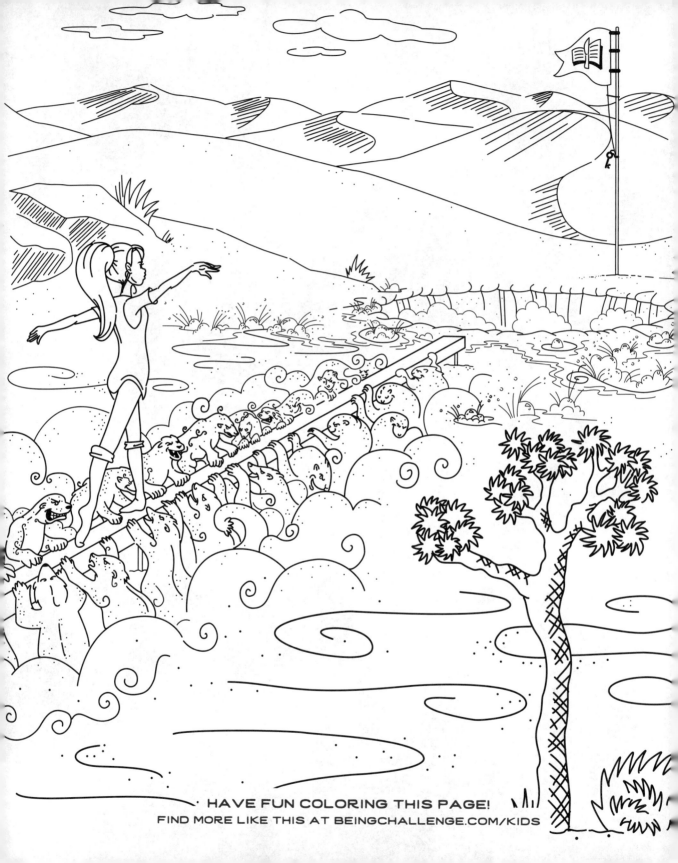

# THE SANDS OF REDVALE

## PART 3

"Melchior!" Emily shouted.

She dashed toward the open door and took a soaring leap, wrapping her arms around the long neck of their camel friend. Melchior had helped lead them through the desert on their last trip to Redvale.

Malachi, Aiden, Isabella, and Red were right behind Emily, beaming with delight. They were followed by the Redvale villagers, who poured out of the building.

"It's so good to see you again!" Emily exclaimed. "Are you going with us to find the Sand Castle?"

"Wouldn't miss it for the world," said Melchior.

"We're gonna need him," said Red. "We wouldn't be able to carry the big red box through the desert without Melchior's help."

"But the Sand Box weighs a ton! You're going to hurt yourself trying to carry it," Emily said. Melchior was already loaded down with supplies—food, blankets, tents, and loads of water. How could he carry any more?

"Don't worry about me," said the camel. "They say it's the straw that breaks the camel's back. The Sand Box isn't straw, so I'll be okay."

"Make way!" came shouts from behind. Emily spun around to see four villagers carrying the big chest containing who knows what. They placed the Sand Box on a sled, which was then connected to Melchior. The camel was going to drag it behind as they went.

"Climb aboard," said Melchior to Emily and Red.

"All right!" said the fox, as Melchior folded his lanky legs beneath him and lowered himself to the ground. Red scrambled onto his back, soon followed by Emily. They squeezed into the saddle.

Villagers blew on silver trumpets and clapped and cheered. "Godspeed!" several people shouted. Malachi handed a backpack full of supplies to Aiden and binoculars to Emily. Then the tiny group took off, heading north into the Red Desert.

"May the prayers of Cherryfield strengthen our steps," Malachi said.

With those words, they ventured deep into the wilderness. The flag of Peter, which was attached to Melchior's side, flapped in the breeze.

# SANDPAPER

After the first hour, it was Isabella's turn to ride on Melchior's back, and she rocked with the swaying motion of the camel.

"I still don't get how we're going to find the other flags in a vast desert like this," she said.

"No worries. I've got my Big Wilderness Guidebook," Malachi said, slipping the huge book from a pouch attached to Melchior's side. The last time they were in Redvale, the Guidebook led them through desert, mountains, forest, swamp, and sea. "The Guidebook never lets us down. It will take us from flag to flag."

Malachi opened to the middle of the book and then flipped through the pages. Suddenly, he let out a gasp. From Isabella's perch on top of the camel, she saw that one of the book's pages appeared to have turned completely brown. It was covered with what looked like speckly sand.

"Oooo, that doesn't look right," Red pointed out.

"It's not right," Malachi said. "Some of the pages of the Big Wilderness Guidebook are turning to sandpaper! We have less time than I thought."

"What if all of the pages in the Guidebook turn to sandpaper?" Isabella asked. "Does that mean we'll have no way to find the flags?"

"There's always a way," Malachi said. "Have faith."

But Isabella wasn't so sure. Without the Guidebook, they might wind up wandering in the desert until they run out of food and water. The others must have had similar worries because everyone went quiet for the next fifteen minutes. Not until…

"I see a flag!" Aiden shouted.

Sure enough, off in the distance they could see a flag flapping in the warm wind. When they got closer, Isabella noticed that the flag displayed the picture of three money sacks and an ax.

"We're on the right path," Malachi said, checking his Guidebook. "This is the flag of Matthew, the disciple of Jesus who once worked as a tax collector. The three money sacks in the picture represent the taxes he collected."

"And the ax?" asked Aiden.

"Sadly, it's believed he was killed by a battle ax."

"Oh," Isabella said. First she was nervous. But now she was really depressed.

"You've been having a hard time since the last time I saw you, haven't you?" Malachi said, slipping up beside Isabella.

"*Everyone* is having a tough time back at home," she said from atop Melchior's back. "The coronavirus forced us to cancel school."

"You know full well that's not the problem I'm talking about."

Malachi always seemed to know what was going on with her, so she decided she might as well not hide it.

After hemming and hawing, Isabella said, "I told my best friends at school about our journey to Redvale. But I think a couple of boys overheard…and, well… they started making fun of me. Now, almost my entire class thinks I'm some kind of weirdo, claiming to have gone to another world. That's not a good way to impress people at a new school."

"Is impressing people your goal?"

"Um…I suppose not. But I was at least hoping kids at my new school wouldn't think I'm crazy."

"Is that why you tried to convince yourself that your first visit to Redvale never really happened?"

*How did he know?*

Melchior craned his long neck around to look at Isabella. "I know exactly how you feel."

"You do?"

"When Malachi first told me about the king across the sea, I didn't believe him."

"What changed?"

"I met the king in person. Your life is never the same once you stand in the presence of the king."

"I stood in the presence of the king during our last trip to Redvale, so what's my excuse?" Isabella said. "I betrayed Redvale and the king by trying to tell myself that this world didn't exist."

"It's hard to face terrible teasing like you did," Malachi said. "It's especially difficult when your first trip to Redvale becomes a distant memory. That's why we called you back here again. To help strengthen the foundations of your faith."

"I thought we were called here to stop the world from turning to sand."

"Same thing. You need to build your life on a strong foundation—and one of those is Scripture. You also stopped carrying your Bible with you back at home, didn't you?"

Isabella hung her head. But there was no use denying it. "Yes. I just didn't want to give kids more reason to tease me."

"You even gave up gymnastics. Why?"

"I was just feeling so lousy about things, I didn't want to put myself in any situation where I could be embarrassed. Especially at a new school."

Malachi reached out and patted her on the arm. "'Do not conform to the pattern of this world.' You remember that Bible verse, don't you?"

Isabella nodded. She used to do a lot of Bible memorization—but not so much anymore.

"Do you remember the entire verse?" Melchior asked.

"Do not conform to the pattern of this world, but be transformed by the renewing of your mind," said Isabella. "Then you will be able to test and approve what God's will is—his good, pleasing, and perfect will."

Malachi grinned. "Excellent! Today, it's time for you to be transformed by the renewing of your mind, and we're going to help. That's why I'm giving the first mission to you, Isabella!"

"To me?"

"That's right. It's going to be dangerous, so get ready to take the leap of your life."

*Dangerous? A leap?* Isabella didn't like the sound of that.

## THE BALANCE BEAM

Soon, the caravan reached the third flag, this one showing a basket containing loaves of bread.

"It's the flag of the disciple Philip," Malachi said. "Before Jesus multiplied the loaves and the fish, He asked Philip where they could find food to feed everyone."

"We keep finding these flags, but why haven't we found the next key to open the Sand Box?" Red asked, furiously digging in the sand next to the flag of Philip. "I thought we're supposed to find keys at these flags."

"Not yet," Malachi said. "The Guidebook says we'll find a key at the next flag. Isabella will retrieve it."

"Isabella?" Aiden said. "Why does she get to go first? That's not fair!"

"It's not about fairness. She has been *called* to get the second key."

"I really don't mind if Aiden retrieves the key, since he wants to so badly," Isabella said.

"*I mind.* Aiden, you'll wait your turn."

"But why choose Isabella?" Emily asked. "Before we came here, she didn't even know if she believed in Redvale anymore!"

"All the more reason for Isabella to complete this mission, Emily."

"But she…I don't know…She…What if she fails?"

As Emily spoke those words, Isabella had a sinking feeling. Did her little sister not believe she could do this?

"She will not be tested beyond which she can bear," Malachi said. "Besides, I think she needs your encouragement, not your doubts, Emily."

"I suppose so," said Emily, kicking at the sand. Then she tried to work up some phony enthusiasm. "You can do it, Isabella!"

Her words didn't make Isabella feel any better about what lay ahead.

When they eventually spotted the fourth flag, Malachi brought them to a halt well before they reached it. He crouched and studied the ground, picking up a handful of sand and letting it seep through his fingers.

"Why did we stop?" Red asked. "Let's just stroll up to that flag and grab the key." The little fox strode in the direction of the flag.

"Stop, Red!" Malachi tried to reach out and grab Red by the tail. But the fox was too fast.

"This will be a piece of cake!" Red said. But as the fox pressed forward, he went slower and slower and slower—until his legs could no longer move. He became mired in the sand. It was like walking through concrete.

"Help! Help! I think I'm in quicksand!"

"It's not quicksand," Malachi said. "It's slowsand."

"Very funny," said Red.

"I'm not being funny. This sand is designed to slow down any one trying to reach the flag. It will take you about seventy years to walk through the slowsand and reach the flag."

"Seventy years! I don't have that kind of time! Help!"

"Aiden and Emily, tie a rope to Melchior and throw it to Red. While you pull him out, I'll prepare Isabella for her mission."

Isabella felt a lump of tension in her stomach.

"If there's slowsand all around the flag, how in the world am I going to reach the key?" Isabella asked. "I don't have seventy years either."

"There's a narrow path through the slowsand," Malachi said.

"How narrow?"

"Four inches wide."

"That's pretty narrow."

"It's the same width as a balance beam." Malachi gave her a wink. The balance beam was Isabella's specialty in gymnastics at their old school before they moved.

By this time, the others had pulled Red out of the slowsand, and the little fox was stomping around, muttering about getting sand in his ears. Malachi led Isabella to the edge of the dangerous sand. Sure enough, a long balance beam ran only inches above the ground. It looked about four inches wide, just as he said, and it stretched almost all of the way to the flag.

"Whoa, that's narrow!" Aiden exclaimed, striding up to them. "I sure hope you don't fall off, like you did in your last balance-beam competition."

"*Aiden!*" Malachi said, giving him a glare. "Not helping."

"Sorry," Aiden said. "Don't worry, Isabella. You can do it!"

Again, not very enthusiastic encouragement. But Isabella understood what he was getting at. She didn't think she could succeed either.

# SAND BADGERS

Isabella stood at the edge of the balance beam, trying to work up the courage to take the first step.

"Wait," said Malachi. "There's a few things you need to know before you begin. First, don't be bothered by the Sand Badgers."

"The what?"

"As you walk across the beam, Sand Badgers are going to nip at your feet and try to knock you off. But because they're made of sand, they can't really bite or grab you. Just keep your eyes on the flag and your mind on Scripture. Think of the Bible verses you used to memorize. Fill your mind with them, and they'll change your heart. You'll also block out the words of the Sand Badgers."

"They talk?"

"Way too much."

"Finally, at the end of the Narrow Beam, you'll have to jump across the Great Abyss to reach the flag."

Isabella didn't like the sound of that. "What's a Great Abyss?"

"It's a deep hole. But 'Great Abyss' sounds much more impressive."

"How deep?"

"You don't want to know. But it's not a wide hole. You can jump it. No problem."

*No problem?*

"Remember your Scripture," Malachi said. "It will strengthen your spirit and guide your feet."

Isabella nodded. Then Emily hugged her and Aiden gave her a pat on the back. Melchior whispered in her ear, "Keep your eyes on the prize."

Standing at the edge of the slowsand, Isabella took off her shoes. When walking a balance beam, it's best to do it barefoot. Then she took a deep breath and stepped onto the beam.

Isabella tried to remember what her gymnastics coach used to tell her. She said to focus your eyes on a point in the distance—just as Malachi said. Isabella kept her gaze on the flag and extended her arms to the side, like wings. Stomach in, body tall, chin up. With each step, she placed her foot down toes first, then the heel. So far so good. This wasn't so bad.

"She's gonna fall, she's gonna fall!"

Those words erupted at her feet, giving her a start. She knew she wasn't supposed to look down, but she couldn't help it. She stared at her feet and saw dozens of brown badgers emerging from the sand. They were trying to nip at her ankles, and they kept chattering.

"Bite her! Knock her off! She's gonna fall! She's gonna fall! Look out! Timber!"

Isabella was so startled that she nearly took a tumble. She had to put out one leg to keep her balance and moved her arms like a windmill.

"Look! She's gonna fall! AHHHHHH!"

*Focus, focus, focus.* Slowly, she brought herself back into a standing position. The badgers swarmed her feet, but when they tried to bite, all she felt was the rough scratch of sand. She was okay. She hoped.

Isabella continued, placing one foot after another.

"Where's your Bible, nerd girl?" one of the Sand Badgers said, once again nearly sending her into a free fall. The badger's voice sounded exactly like a neighbor boy who constantly teased her.

She remembered what Malachi said. Keep the Bible in your head, and it will change your heart. So, she dug deep in her memory for all of the verses she had memorized over the years.

"I keep my eyes always on the LORD," she said out loud, trying to block the chattering of the Sand Badgers. "With him at my right hand, I will not be shaken. Psalm 16:8."

"Listen to that! Nerd girl is reciting the Bible!" said a Sand Badger.

"She thinks she's so holy!"

"She thinks she's too good for us!"

"Watch out! You're falling!"

"The LORD is close to the brokenhearted and saves those who are crushed in spirit. Psalm 34:18." That verse was always special to Isabella. She thought of it whenever her heart was broken. Which seemed to be quite often.

"Why don't you go back to your old school?" said another badger, once again imitating the voice of one of the boys at her new school.

"Get away from me!" she screamed, kicking at the badger. The move nearly threw her off balance and sent her sprawling, but she caught herself in time.

*Concentrate. Concentrate. Eyes on the flag.*

"Be strong and courageous. Do not be afraid or terrified because of them, for the LORD goes with you; he will never leave you nor forsake you. Deuteronomy... WHOAAHHHH!"

Isabella very nearly stepped off the edge of the beam. She had reached the end, and just in front of her was a deep, dark hole. The Great Abyss.

"Push her into the Abyss! Push her off!"

The badgers tried to shove her into the Abyss, but their bodies just crumbled to sand. They couldn't hurt her. She knew that now. She stared down into the chasm. If she fell in...Now *that* could hurt her. Was there even a bottom to the hole?

The hole was about five feet across, and she would have to jump it. It looked possible, if she got a running start. She backed up several steps. This would be a simple balance-beam dismount. She'd done it many times before, but she'd never dismounted over a gaping hole miles deep.

Isabella decided on a simple round-off dismount. She raised both hands above her head and rushed forward. Then she reached down and put both hands on the end of the beam. When both of her feet were sticking high up in the air, she pushed off! As she launched herself over the Abyss, head over heels, she saw nothing but deep darkness and swallowing sand, cascading into the hole like a waterfall. Then she hit solid ground with both feet, her arms outstretched in salute.

She had done it! Off in the distance, she could hear the others cheering wildly.

"Way to go!" Emily yelled.

"I give you a perfect 10!" Aiden called.

Then it hit her. It was one thing doing a dismount off of the beam. How was she going to jump back onto it to get back? Before she could worry about that, she had a job to do. The ground on this side of the Abyss looked solid enough, so she walked right up to the flag. The flag showed the picture of an open Bible, with a knife between the pages.

Attached to a hook on the flagpole was a golden key, with the image of a Bible on it. Isabella reached out, put her hand on the key, and lifted. Suddenly, the ground began to shake, like an earthquake.

"What have I done?" she shouted.

The rocking and rolling hurled her to the ground, and it felt as if the world was tilting on its side. She rolled toward the edge of the Great Abyss, and she realized she wasn't going to be able to stop herself from tumbling into the hole. The last thing she saw before she closed her eyes were the fierce faces of a dozen angry Sand Badgers.

Then quiet. Stillness. She blinked and opened her eyes. She was still alive, lying face down in the sand. The ground had stopped shaking.

Raising her head, she spit out sand and looked around. The Sand Badgers were gone. The Abyss had disappeared. She had a hunch that even the slowsand had been transformed into solid ground, all in the blink of an eye.

This was confirmed when Malachi and the others raced in her direction. She didn't know how in the world she had done it, but she had succeeded! Her right hand was clenched in a fist at her side. She brought it to her face and slowly opened her hand.

Isabella smiled. She was clutching the second key.

# TO BE CONTINUED ON PAGE 130.

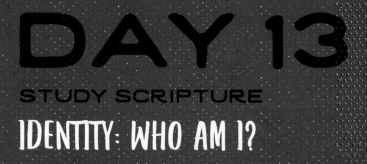

# DAY 13
## STUDY SCRIPTURE
## IDENTITY: WHO AM I?

### WHO WAS JESUS?

One day, Jesus asked His disciples who they say He is. Peter declared, "You are the Messiah!"

Bingo! Peter was right on target.

Then Jesus told them that His mission was to go to Jerusalem, where He would be killed and rise again in three days. When Peter heard this, he shouted, **"Never, Lord! This shall never happen to you!" Matthew 16:22.**

Furious, Jesus shouted at Peter, **"Get behind me, Satan!"**

Why was Jesus so angry? And why would he call Peter "Satan"? Strong words.

The reason for the anger is that Jesus knew His mission was to die on the cross for each and every one of us. In a way, Peter was tempting Jesus, trying to tell Him that He didn't need to die.

But Jesus knew He couldn't skip the cross. He knew exactly who He was, and what He came to earth to do.

# WHO ARE YOU?

Jesus knew who He was, and He knew His mission. Do you know your mission in life? As we grow up, there are many ways we try to figure out our purpose in life. We do this by...

- Trying things on our own to find out if we like them or not

- Comparing ourselves to friends and classmates to see if we're good at something

- Listening to what our guardians or parents say about us

- Noticing things we like and don't like in books, movies, and apps

To explore who you are, answer the questions below. Talk about them in a group or think about them alone.

WHAT DO YOUR <u>FRIENDS</u> <u>AND PARENTS</u> SAY YOU'RE GOOD AT DOING?

WHAT DO <u>OTHER</u> PEOPLE SAY YOU SHOULD BE WHEN YOU GROW UP?

WHAT DO <u>OTHERS</u> THINK ARE YOUR FAVORITE THINGS TO DO?

WHAT DO <u>YOU</u> THINK YOU'RE GOOD AT DOING?

WHEN YOU GROW UP, WHAT DO <u>YOU</u> WANT TO DO?

WHAT DO <u>YOU</u> SAY ARE YOUR FAVORITE THINGS TO DO?

# WHO DOES THE BIBLE SAY YOU ARE?

The Scriptures reveal our "identity"—who we are. Therefore, the most important way to discover who we are is by reading the Bible. Read the following five verses out loud. What do they mean to you?

**1 GOD MADE YOU**

**John 1:3—Through him all things were made; without him nothing was made that has been made.**

The world is called "the creation" because there is a Creator. God made it all. Including you.

**2 GOD LOVES YOU**

**John 3:16—For God so loved the world that he gave his one and only Son, that whoever believes in him shall not perish but have eternal life.**

God loves you so much that He even watched His Son, Jesus, die on the cross in your place.

**3 GOD CALLS YOU HIS CHILD**

**1 John 3:1a—See what great love the Father has lavished on us, that we should be called children of God! And that is what we are!**

Many inventors name their creations after themselves. Rudolf Diesel invented the diesel engine, George G.W. Ferris created the Ferris wheel, and the Jacuzzi brothers invented the Jacuzzi.

Because God made you, He gets to name you. And He calls you His "child."

## 4 YOU ARE CHOSEN AND SENT TO MAKE A DIFFERENCE IN THE WORLD.

**1 Peter 2:9—But you are a chosen people, a royal priesthood, a holy nation, God's special possession, that you may declare the praises of him who called you out of darkness into his wonderful light.**

God chose you. He called you into His light to declare His praises.

## 5 YOU HAVE INHERITED ETERNAL LIFE IN HEAVEN

**1 Peter 1:3-4—Praise be to the God and Father of our Lord Jesus Christ! In his great mercy he has given us new birth into a living hope through the resurrection of Jesus Christ from the dead, and into an inheritance that can never perish, spoil or fade. This inheritance is kept in heaven for you...**

To "inherit," means to receive something when someone dies. When Jesus died for us, we inherited eternal life in heaven. What a wonderful gift!

# TARGET PRACTICE

Here you will find four targets, each with three circles. Answer each question by coloring in the ring that connects to your answer:

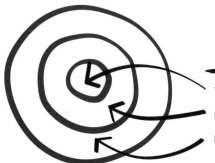

## DO YOU HAVE A BIBLE?
### (IT COULD BE A CHILDREN'S BIBLE OR BIBLE STORY BOOK.)

YES

MAYBE, I'M NOT SURE.

NO

# RED ALERT!

The first five books of the Bible (Genesis, Exodus, Leviticus, Numbers, Deuteronomy) are sometimes called the Pentateuch. "Pentateuch" comes from Greek words that mean "five scrolls."

## HOW OFTEN DO YOU READ YOUR BIBLE?

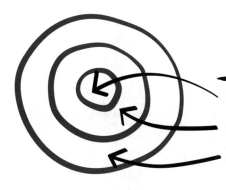

EVERY DAY (6 TO 7 TIMES A WEEK)

SOMETIMES (2 TO 5 TIMES A WEEK)

ALMOST NEVER (0 TO 1 TIME A WEEK)

## DO YOU UNDERSTAND WHAT YOU READ IN YOUR BIBLE?

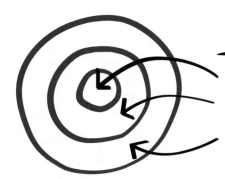

ALWAYS

SOMETIMES

NEVER, IT'S SO CONFUSING!

## DO YOU TAKE YOUR BIBLE WITH YOU TO CHURCH?

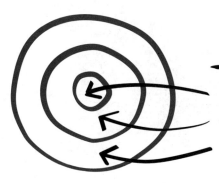

ALWAYS

SOMETIMES

NEVER

# DAY 14

## THE 4 Rs

### OUR TREASURE

Before the printing press was invented, Bibles had to be copied by hand. One word at a time!

Scribes would sit in "scriptoriums," dipping their goose quills (pens) in ink and writing out every single word of the Bible. They worked six hours a day, sometimes longer. Their wrists must have ached!

Thankfully, Johannes Gutenberg changed the world with his printing press in the 1450s. Forty-nine of the Bibles that he printed still exist today, and they are thought to be some of the most valuable books in the entire world.

Until the printing press, very few people owned a Bible all their own. The first children's Bible in America was not published until 1763. So if you own a Bible, you have a treasure. God speaks to us from the pages of our Bibles.

Before Jesus's time, the Israelites' Scripture was what we call today the Old Testament. Here is what God said to the Israelites about the Scriptures.

**"These commandments that I give you today are to be on your hearts. Impress them on your children. Talk about them when you sit at home and when you walk along the road, when you lie down and when you get up. Tie them as symbols on your hands and bind them on your foreheads. Write them on the doorframes of your houses and on your gates."**
**Deuteronomy 6:6-9**

Jesus wants the Bible to be an important part of our lives. To make this happen, learn the 4 Rs of the Bible, which come from Rick Warren's book, *The Purpose Driven Life.*

**READ**—Regularly read the Scriptures or have it read to you.

**REMEMBER**—Memorize Bible verses or recall Bible stories.

**RESEARCH**—Learn all you can about the Bible and what it says.

**REFLECT**—When you read a Bible passage, think about what it means to you and what it says about the things you're currently experiencing.

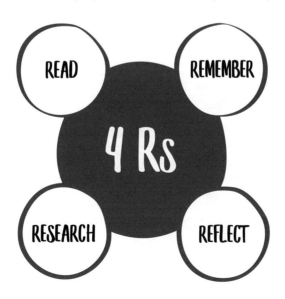

# HOW DO YOU LEARN?

Kids learn in different ways. How good you are in the 4 R's can depend on your personality. For instance, some kids are better at using their senses (seeing, smelling, tasting, touching, and hearing) to learn about the world. They notice little details and like instructions when they build things. They're more interested in what's happening now than in the future, and they like to collect all of the facts before starting a project.

If that sounds like you, then you might find it easier to Research and Remember the Bible.

Other kids enjoy using their imagination and gathering ideas. They're interested in new and different things. They dream about the future and imagine all the possibilities. They're better at imagining new ways to think about things than memorizing facts.

If that sounds like you, then you might find it easier to Read and Reflect on the Bible. One way is not better than the other. These are just different ways of learning.

If you want to discover more about the way you learn, check out our "What's My Personality" questionnaire on our website: www.beingchallenge.com/kidsresources

**"Oh, how I love your law! I meditate on it all day long!" Psalm 119:97**

# CHALLENGE

Read or have someone read out loud the short Bible story below. This story comes from Genesis 11, but it's not the exact words.

*Years after the flood, people began to move from place to place. When they reached the land of Babylon, they decided to settle there and build a tower so high that it would reach the sky. The hearts of the people were proud, and they thought they could reach the same level as God, the Highest.*

*This pride was their downfall. When God came down to the city and saw what the people were doing, He became very angry. He decided to put a stop to their construction by making sure they couldn't understand each other. Suddenly, people began to speak different languages. When they tried to communicate, it turned into a babble of confused voices.*

*Soon, people spread across the world, taking their different languages with them. The tower they tried to build is called the tower of "Babel." Some people think this is where we get the word "babble." But others say there is no connection, even though the words sound the same. They say "babble" came from the "ba-ba-ba" sound of babies.*

Next, do one or both of the following two activities. If you do both, pay attention to which one you like better.

# ACTIVITY 1

Answer these questions:

**1** What was the name of the land the people settled in?

_____

**2** What did God want to stop when He confused their languages?

_____

**3** What word sounds like it has to do with the Tower of Babel?

_____

# ACTIVITY 2

Tell someone the moral of the story from memory. Or write out below what the story was about:

_____

_____

_____

If you preferred Activity #1, you might be stronger in Researching and Remembering. If you preferred Activity #2, you might prefer Reading and Reflecting.

# RED ALERT!

After the Pentateuch, the Old Testament has 12 historical books. These books of the Bible tell about the Promised Land, as well as the Kings and Judges of Israel—and much more.

#BEINGCHALLENGEKIDS

# DAY 15

## MAKE ROOM FOR THE BIBLE

---

### AND THE MESSIEST ROOM AWARD GOES TO...

Believe it or not, two sisters won an award in 2019 for having the messiest bedroom in all of England. When you look at the photo of the winning room, it's impossible to see the floor. The room is piled high with clothes and toys. For all they know, there could be a family of hobbits living under all of that stuff.

Even though your room might not win any awards for being the messiest in the country, some of you are probably still quite messy. Others might be extremely organized.

When it comes to reading the Bible, our personality types show through. Just like our bedrooms, some of us are very organized in our Bible reading. Others... not so much.

But whether you're organized or not, it helps to have some kind of plan for reading the Bible. We all need to make room for the Bible in our lives.

# SPONTANEOUS OR ORGANIZED

Ask yourself…which of these two groups do you fall into—Organized Kids or Spontaneous Kids? ("Spontaneous" means doing things without much of a plan.)

**ORGANIZED KIDS** like to sort books and keep toys in order. They finish projects, feel better when they arrive places on time (or early), know what they like, and make decisions quickly.

**SPONTANEOUS KIDS** go with the flow, change plans at the last minute, love to be surprised, follow their curiosity, and love lots of options.

If you're a Spontaneous Kid and don't like plans, it might be harder for you to find time to read the Bible than for an Organized Kid. But whatever you're like, you need the Bible in your life because it's one of the places where we meet Jesus.

So don't hide your light under a bushel. And don't bury your Bible under a stack of dirty clothes and old pizza boxes.

# BEING WITH JESUS, BEING LIKE JESUS

When you dig into your Bible, you're BEING with God. You're BEING with Jesus.

But remember, reading the Bible is not just about hearing the words of Jesus. It's about imitating His actions. It's also about BEING like Jesus.

BEING like Jesus takes faith, which is a gift that only God can give to us. It's not something you can get on your own strength. Faith leads to actions.

When we try to live like Jesus, we'll constantly fail, of course. We could live a million years and still not be able to live just like Him. But He knows that. That's why Jesus is our Savior. He picks us up when we fall. He'll help us become the person we were created to be.

## SO WHO DO YOU WANT TO BECOME?

You've probably been asked, "What do you want to be when you grow up?" That's an important question. But an even more important question is: Who do I want to become?

Right now, take a moment to answer that question.

**I WANT TO BE A PERSON WHO IS...**

_____

_____

_____

_____

Many famous people in this world have seen their wildest dreams come true. They're rich. They have big houses. But they're still sad and lonely. That's because some people get what they want in life, but they never discover who they are—a child of God.

No matter how much we have, if we do not have God as our Father, we'll feel as if we're missing something. We'll be like a puzzle with the most important pieces missing.

Only God can tell you who you are. No one else can do it. So turn to your Bible and BE with your Father in Heaven. Let Him fill in those missing pieces.

# CHALLENGE

How do you read your Bible? On a scale of 1 to 10, how much do you plan your Bible reading?

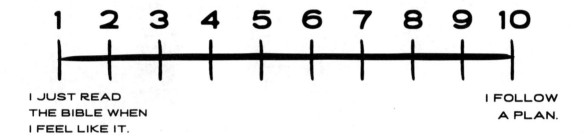

I JUST READ
THE BIBLE WHEN
I FEEL LIKE IT.

I FOLLOW
A PLAN.

If you need help reading the Bible, try setting up a reading plan. There are some helpful Bible apps for kids out there. You can also find some great Bible reading plans on our website: www.beingchallenge.com/kidsresources

**MY BIBLE READING PLAN IS:**

_____

_____

_____

_____

**NOTE**: If you'd like to find out if you're Organized or Spontaneous, check out our "What's My Personality?" questionnaire found on our website: www.beingchallenge.com/kidsresources

# DAY 16

## THE UNCHANGING MESSAGE

### MODERN MIRACLES

Best-selling author Lee Strobel tells the story of Barbara, a woman diagnosed with multiple sclerosis and close to dying. According to Strobel's book, *The Case for Miracles*, Barbara was curled up in bed, nearly blind, and unable to walk. She had a tube in her throat to help her breathe and a tube in her stomach for nourishment. One of her lungs didn't work and her muscles were wasting away.

When her story was told on a Chicago radio station, about 450 people at the Moody Bible Institute decided to pray for her. Then, on Pentecost Sunday, Barbara says she heard a voice from the corner of her room tell her, "My child, get up and walk."

Barbara obeyed. She jumped out of bed and disconnected the oxygen. All of her symptoms went away immediately. Her leg muscles strengthened, she could see, her feet and fingers straightened—and she walked. The doctors were amazed! They had never seen anything like it.

## MIRACLES IN THE BIBLE

There are many stories like Barbara's, and they happen day after day all over the world.

The Bible is also loaded with miracle stories. However, some people have trouble understanding the Bible because certain stories may not make sense to them. Because the stories took place thousands of years ago, there may not be proof beyond the Bible.

It might be hard to explain how Jonah lived inside the belly of a whale, how the Red Sea parted, or how the Nile River turned to blood. Many scientists are Christians, and they try to help people understand these wonderful stories. But understanding these stories is not what brings us faith. The Holy Spirit works in us to help us believe and have faith.

God also gave us the proof of the empty tomb, the greatest miracle of them all. Historic evidence shows that Jesus really did live. He really did die. And He really did rise from the dead.

## BIBLE READING GUIDE

1 Read the whole chapter of the Bible.

2 Ask:

- Who wrote this?

- Who was it written to?

- What was going on?

- Does the verse line up with the overall message of the Bible?

3 Pray for God's insight and wisdom.

4 Talk to your pastor, parent, guardian, or teacher about your questions.

RLC BEING KIDS

# THE SAME YESTERDAY, TODAY, AND FOREVER

Mark the scientific statements below as True or False. (The answers are at the bottom of this page.)

**1** The earth is flat. _____

**2** The sun makes up 99.86% of the solar system's mass. _____

**3** The atom is the smallest particle. _____

**4** A candle flame typically burns at 1,800 degrees Fahrenheit. _____

**5** Heavy objects fall faster than light objects. _____

All of these scientific statements were once considered true at some point in history, and some are still true today. Science changes over time as new information is discovered. For instance, 500 years before Jesus was born, Greek philosophers began to say the Earth was round, not flat. Later, science proved it.

Science is always changing, but the message of the Bible is unchanging. God sent Jesus, His Son, into the world to live a perfect life. He died on the cross, and the punishment for our sins fell on Him. By His suffering and resurrection, we are brought back into a right relationship with God.

The Bible is all about God keeping His unchanging promises. These promises are called "covenants," and there are five of them in Scripture.

- God promised Noah He would never again destroy all living creatures. (Genesis 8:21-22)

- He promised Abraham (who was then called "Abram") he would have many children, and they would be given a new land. (Genesis 15:1-7)

- He promised Moses that He'll make the Israelites into a great nation, **"my treasured possession."** (Exodus 19:3-6)

- He promised David He would establish a kingdom through David's offspring. (2 Samuel 7:8-16)

- He promised that Jesus will usher in a New Covenant, which will set us free from our sins. (Hebrews 9:15)

As the Bible makes clear, God keeps His Word. He keeps His promises. When everything around us is changing and so confusing, He is the solid rock on whom we can rely. We can have faith.

# CHALLENGE

Cut out the bookmark on the left and keep it in your Bible. Whenever you don't understand something in the Bible, take a look at the five steps listed on the bookmark. Then, whenever you're confused about Scripture, go through the steps.

# DAY 17
## STUDY SCRIPTURE
# KNOW THE TRUTH

---

## 7,000 LANGUAGES!

By the year 2025, the goal is for the Bible to be available in every single language in the world, according to the Wycliffe Bible Institute. There are over 7,000 known languages in the world, so that's quite a stack of books!

Below is the same Bible verse translated into a few of those languages. Try saying some of them out loud. Then try to guess what Bible verse you're reading. (The answer is on the bottom of page 119.)

### AFRIKAANS

Want so life het God die wêreld gehad, dat Hy sy eniggebore Seun gegee het, sodat elkeen wat in Hom glo, nie verlore mat gaan nie, maar die ewige lewe kan hê.

### FRENCH

Car Dieu a tant aimé le monde qu'il a donné son fils unique, afin que quiconque croit en lui ne pas périr, mais ait la vie éternelle.

### SPANISH

Porque tanto amó Dios al mundo que ha dado a su hijo unigénito, que todo aquel que cree en él no debe pierda, mas tenga vida eterna.

Đoi voi Thiên Chúa yêu thuong the mà ông đã cho ông chi begotten Son, mà he ai tin Ngài nên không hu mat, nhung có cuoc song mai mai.

# SHEEP AREN'T SO DUMB AFTER ALL

Sheep are often thought of as pretty dumb animals. But they're smart enough to recognize the voice of their shepherd. Jesus told a story to help us understand this:

> **"The one who enters by the gate is the shepherd of the sheep. The gatekeeper opens the gate for him, and the sheep listen to his voice. He calls his own sheep by name and leads them out. When he has brought out all his own, he goes on ahead of them, and his sheep follow him because they know his voice. But they will never follow a stranger; in fact, they will run away from him because they do not recognize a stranger's voice." John 10:2-5**

Jesus is our Good Shepherd. When we read the Bible, we're like sheep learning to recognize His voice. The more we read and hear God's Word, the easier it is for us to recognize when something doesn't sound right. The Bible contains truth. In fact, the Bible is truth—timeless truth.

If we memorize the sound of our Shepherd's voice, we'll be able to run away from teachings and other things that don't sound right. We can compare, or test, what we hear with what we learned and memorized in God's Word.

As it says in 1 John 4:1, **"Dear friends, do not believe every spirit, but test the spirits to see whether they are from God, because many false prophets have gone out into the world."**

# REMEMBERING

Memorizing Scripture plants God's truth in our hearts and minds. Here are some helpful ways to memorize God's Word:

**1** Start small.

**2** Repeat, repeat, repeat!

**3** Write the verse on paper.

**4** Understand what it means.

**5** Know where to find the verse in the Bible.

The following are some good verses to memorize, along with the truth they teach.

| TRUTH | BIBLE VERSE |
| --- | --- |
| God is always with us. | And surely I am with you always, even to the very end of the age. **(Matthew 28:20b)** |
| We do not have to be afraid. | **So do not fear, for I am with you; do not be dismayed, for I am your God. (Isaiah 41:10a)** |
| Jesus is the One true way to heaven. | **Jesus answered, "I am the way and the truth and the life. No one comes to the Father except through me." (John 14:6)** |
| Everyone has sinned. | **...for all have sinned and fall short of the glory of God. (Romans 3:23)** |

| TRUTH | BIBLE VERSE |
|---|---|
| Jesus died for us even though we were sinners. | **But God demonstrates his own love for us in this: While we were yet still sinners, Christ died for us. (Romans 5:8)** |
| Jesus forgave you, so forgive others. | **Be kind to one another, tenderhearted, forgiving one another, as God in Christ forgave you. (Ephesians 4:32, ESV)** |

# CHALLENGE

Memorize a verse this week. You can choose a verse from the chart above, or find another verse. Remember to follow the five steps on page 118.

## WRITE YOUR MEMORY VERSE HERE:

_____

_____

_____

_____

_____

_____

_____

**Answer Key**
John 3:16—For God so loved the world that he gave his only begotten Son, that whoever believes in him should not perish but have everlasting life.

# DAY 18

## STUDY SCRIPTURE

# GOD CAN CHANGE YOUR HEART AND MIND

## SHIPWRECKED!

John Newton was sure he was going to die. His ship had been caught in the grip of a fierce storm for over a week. The ship was splintering apart and barely staying afloat.

Newton's life was also a wreck. Over the years, he had carried slaves on his ship and led a life of terrible sin. But in the midst of this storm at sea, he remembered a Bible passage his mother had taught him—Proverbs 1:24-31. These verses describe what can happen when you don't listen to God. Calamity will strike like a storm and disaster will sweep over you like a whirlwind.

Newton cried out to God for mercy, and he did survive that storm. He then began to study the Bible. One verse that hit home was Luke 11:13, which said that God is like a Father who wants to give good gifts to His children.

Not only did Newton become a Christian, but he stopped selling slaves. He even wrote a booklet that influenced William Wilberforce, the man who led the movement to end slavery in most of the British Empire.

Today, we remember Newton as the man who wrote the famous hymn, *Amazing Grace*. The first lines of the hymn go like this:

> *Amazing Grace, how sweet the sound*
> *That saved a wretch like me.*
> *I once was lost, but now am found*
> *Was blind but now I see.*

God used both the storm and Scripture to change Newton's mind. God also changed his heart.

## CHANGING FROM THE INSIDE OUT

The Bible includes stories that touch our hearts, and it has deep lessons that light up our minds. The more we read, remember, research, and reflect on God's Word, the more it will change us from the inside out.

When I READ about the grace God has given me, I can't help but give grace to others who have hurt me.

When I REMEMBER how Jesus is coming back for me someday, it gives me joy when things are hard.

When I RESEARCH how generous God has been toward me, I try to be more generous to those around me.

When I REFLECT on God's mission to save the lost, I want to be a part of that mission.

"Now I'm turning you over to God, our marvelous God whose gracious Word can make you into what he wants you to be and give you everything you could possibly need in this community of holy friends." Acts 20:32 (*The Message*)

# FOOD FOR THE HEART AND MIND

In the Old Testament, God told the prophet Ezekiel that He was sending him on a mission to the rebellious Israelites. **"Open your mouth and eat what I give you,"** God told him in Ezekiel 2:8.

Then God handed Ezekiel a scroll. He wanted the prophet to eat a scroll?

Please DON'T eat your Bible. This was a vision, and in the vision, Ezekiel ate the scroll. It tasted good—like honey. This passage tells us that if you take in the words of the Bible, those words become part of us, just like food does. The Word of God will change us.

The delicious peanut butter and jelly sandwich you had for lunch wasn't meant to just sit in your stomach. It will be broken down and sent to all parts of your body to give you strength and help you grow. The sandwich changes you from the inside out. So does the Bible.

As Jesus once said, **"People do not live by bread alone, but by every word that comes from the mouth of God." Matthew 4:4 (*New Living Translation*)**

# CHALLENGE

Spend some time eating (reflecting on) a verse or section of Scripture. Here are some verses you can choose, or you can pick your own passage. Then write your answers on the pizza below.

1 CORINTHIANS 10:13     1 TIMOTHY 4:12     DEUTERONOMY 31:6

ISAIAH 41:10     PSALM 119:9     ISAIAH 40:29-31

EPHESIANS 6:1-3

What is God saying about who He is?

_____
_____
_____

What is God saying about who I am?

_____
_____
_____

How does this verse help me love others?

_____
_____
_____

# DAY 19

## GOD SPEAKS THROUGH SCRIPTURE

### THE TEXT MESSAGE

Imagine you got a text on your phone that reads like this:

> HEY! I HAVE A PROJECT FOR US TO DO LATER. :)

**HOW WOULD YOU FEEL IF THIS TEXT MESSAGE CAME FROM:**

Your best friend? _____

Your teacher? _____

Your mom or dad? _____

The text message means something different, depending on who wrote it.

- If it was from a friend, you might be excited about the adventure he or she has planned for your next sleepover.

- If it was from a teacher, you might worry you're going to be given a big school assignment.

- If it was from a parent, you might wonder what housecleaning project you'll have to do.

Knowing who wrote something makes all the difference in the world.

## AUTHOR UNKNOWN?

The Bible is a collection of 66 books, written over 1,500 years by almost 40 known writers. As we saw in the text-message example, it makes a big difference knowing who wrote each book, who it was written to, and why it was written. That's why it's so important to research, or study, the Bible. (By the way, Jesus didn't write any of the books. But He is at the heart of the Bible.)

## RED ALERT!

After the 4 Gospels and Book of Acts, there are 21 "epistles," or letters in the New Testament. Many of the letters were written by Paul to people and churches across the land. The final book of the Bible is Revelation. It talks about future events in mysterious ways.

# INSPIRED WORDS

In the Christian Church, we believe something called "verbal inspiration." This means that God worked through the writers of the Bible, giving them the thoughts, ideas, and words to write down.

According to 2 Timothy 3:16-17, **"All Scripture is inspired by God and profitable for teaching, for reproof, for correction, for training in righteousness; so that the man of God may be adequate, equipped for every good work."** (*New American Standard Bible*)

Below are some Bible verses where God tells a man specifically what to write down.

King David wrote:
"The Spirit of the Lord spoke through me; his word was on my tongue."
(2 Samuel 23:2)

Jeremiah said that God gave him a command. "Write in a book all the words I have spoken to you." (Jeremiah 30:2b)

Peter, one of Jesus's disciples, told us: "...but holy men of God spoke as they were moved by the Holy Spirit" (2 Peter 1:21b, NKJV)

# ROBOT, I AM NOT!

The writers of the Bible weren't robots, mindlessly writing down words given to them. They knew what they were doing when they were writing. God spoke through men who were kings, peasants, fishermen, teachers, lawyers, doctors, and more to write the books of the Bible. They may not have been professional writers, but they were inspired by God.

In the Bible, God's words were breathed into the lives of great men of faith. Each writer of the Bible used their own voice, chose their own words, and had their own unique style. God didn't erase their personalities when He spoke through them.

# CHALLENGE

Do one or both of these things:

 Fill out the personality questionnaire on the Red Letter Challenge Kids website: www.beingchallenge.com/kidsresources

 Find a way to share Scripture with others. It could be by telling someone about Jesus. It can also be through writing a story or song or drawing a picture and then sharing it with a friend. Or some other way.

KEYSTONE HABIT 3:

# PAUSE

# PRAY

TO

# THE SANDS OF REDVALE

## PART 4

Aiden had never been so amazed by Isabella in all of his life. She just did a near-perfect dismount over a BOTTOMLESS PIT! How incredible was that?

"Thanks to you, Isabella, we now have the Scripture Key," Malachi said, as Isabella handed it to him. He held the key high, and sunlight glimmered on gold.

"Let me insert the key into the Sand Box!" Red said, hopping up and down and trying to snag it from Malachi's hands.

"Remember, the key doesn't work unless you all do it together—Aiden, Isabella, and Emily."

"And me?" Red said.

"Yes, you can help too," said Malachi. "But since Isabella retrieved the key, let her begin."

Malachi handed the key back to Isabella. Then the three kids put their hands together, and Red topped it off with his paw. All together, they inserted the key into the Sand Box and turned it.

CLICK!

"What a sweet sound," Red said. "Two keys down—three to go. Do I get to fetch the next one?"

"Patience, Red. The next mission has been given to Aiden."

Aiden was hoping he'd say that. But now that Malachi actually spoke his name out loud, nervousness crept over him like so many spiders. Isabella had performed marvelously, but what if he failed in his mission? It would be really embarrassing. Everything was a contest to Aiden. He hated losing whenever they played

Monopoly, video games, tag, running, swimming…you name it. So it made him feel a little sick just thinking that Isabella would succeed in her mission and he might not.

"Before we head off for the next key, tell us about this flag," Emily said. The flag where Isabella had found the Scripture Key carried the picture of a Bible and a knife.

"I know this one!" piped up Melchior. "That's the flag of the disciple Bartholomew, because he put great faith in Scripture. He was also killed with a knife."

"That was our fourth flag," Isabella said, counting them on her fingers. "Eight to go."

"Let's move…Onward and upward!" said Malachi, holding up the Big Wilderness Guidebook. "Six more pages have turned to sandpaper, so there's no time to lose."

They continued their trek north, eventually coming across a fifth flag before setting up their tents for the night. This was the flag of Andrew, and it had the picture of two fish and an X-shaped cross. The disciple Andrew, like his brother Peter, was once a fisherman and became a fisher of men for Jesus. He was killed on an X-shaped cross.

"That's why Scotland has a white X against a blue background on its national flag," Malachi pointed out.

Soon, the sun began to set, creating fireworks of yellow, orange, and fiery red on the western horizon. As night set in, they sat around the campfire, eating cheese sandwiches, apples, and figs, while Isabella described what it was like walking the balance beam past the Sand Badgers. Aiden didn't say much, partly because he was growing ever more nervous—and partly because he was getting more and more jealous of his older sister.

He was starting to panic.

# THE STARS

Later that night, when everybody was asleep, Aiden lay on his back, staring at the roof of the tent, his mind still buzzing with worries. Malachi suddenly whispered through the tent flap.

"Come, Aiden, time for us to talk."

Melchior was snoring as Aiden slipped out of his tent and past the camel. He found a seat in the sand by the fire. Malachi sat opposite him, poking at the flames, and sparks flew upward into the star-filled sky. Aiden had never seen so many stars before; there had to be a gazillion, sweeping from horizon to horizon.

"You don't play the trumpet any more, do you, Aiden?" Melchior said, breaking the silence.

"Nah."

"Why'd you quit?"

"Just got bored."

"Are you sure that was it?"

Aiden had a hunch that Malachi knew the real reason he gave up the trumpet. It wasn't just boredom. Emily had become good on the piano, and Isabella was incredible on the violin. When Aiden realized he could never beat them at playing musical instruments, he gave up the trumpet.

But he didn't say any of this. He just shrugged.

"Since your last visit to Redvale, I've been pleased that you've continued your servant ways," Malachi said, mercifully changing the subject. "Until the lockdown, you continued to teach Goggles how to play baseball, and the other boys now accept him."

Aiden grinned. Being praised was like feasting on a big bowl of ice cream.

"You've developed the heart of a servant, but you've neglected one area of BEING like Jesus. Do you know what that might be?"

Aiden shrugged. "Beats me."

"You're a boy of action. You like to serve because it means doing things for others. You're a doer and that's good. But you also need to stop sometimes—and pray."

Aiden scowled. He didn't take criticism easily.

"Do you agree, Aiden? Do you think you need to learn to pray more?"

"Yeah, yeah, yeah. Can we talk about something else now?"

"This is important for you to hear before your mission tomorrow."

"What's prayer got to do with my mission?"

"Everything. Tomorrow, you will be in a battle."

"A battle? Like a real battle? Will I have a weapon? A lightsaber maybe?"

"Your weapon will be the sword of the Spirit," Malachi said.

Aiden's heart sank. "Oh. I thought maybe I'd get a real sword."

"The sword of the Spirit is as real as you get. Tomorrow, your mission is to retrieve the Prayer Key from a flag that will be at the center of a big battle."

"And how will I get to the flag if I don't have a weapon?"

"By listening," Malachi said.

"Listening for what?"

"You'll find out. Just let me offer one piece of advice: Be snared by prayer."

"Be snared by prayer? What's that supposed to mean?"

"You'll figure it out—if you truly listen. Prayer is not just about telling God what you want Him to do. It's about *listening* to Him. So…be snared by prayer."

As Malachi stood and made a move to go back to his tent, Aiden became desperate for answers. "Do you mean God is going to talk to me on the battlefield?"

"God is always talking to us, wherever we are."

"But…hold on…How will I know He's speaking? I don't get it!"

"Good night, Aiden. Remember, prayer can change things. It can even change *you*."

Aiden went to sleep feeling more confused and nervous than ever. *Snared by prayer?* Why in the world did Malachi have to be so mysterious?

# THE BATTLEGROUND

The next morning, following breakfast, they broke camp and left while the air was still relatively cool. After an hour of traveling up and down sand dunes, Aiden saw a distant flag, flapping in a valley between two large dunes.

He also saw soldiers. Lots of soldiers. Two entire armies. One army was positioned on a sand dune to the right of the flag, and the other army had gathered on a dune to the left.

When Malachi spotted the soldiers, he motioned for everyone to get down, including Melchior. They lay on their stomachs, peering down from a high dune.

One of the armies was dressed all in red, while the other army wore green uniforms. There had to be a thousand or more soldiers, some of them sitting atop camels. But here's the truly strange thing. They all seemed to be carrying musical instruments—trombones, trumpets, tubas, and piccolos. The craziest instrument of all was what looked like a monstrous horn-shaped cannon on wheels.

"Are those armies or marching bands?" Isabella asked.

"Both," said Malachi. "The Destroyers control the minds of everyone in these marching bands. They've been turned into enemy armies, fighting over the flag and preventing anyone from reaching it."

"A marching band army?" Aiden asked. "That doesn't seem scary." Maybe his mission wasn't going to be so difficult after all.

"How does an army attack with a trombone?" Emily asked.

"You'd be surprised. They call them 'sandblasters' for a reason."

"This is ridiculous!" Red said. "The key is right in front of us. I'm marching down there and grabbing it!"

"No, Red, I wouldn't—"

Once again, the fox was too fast. He sprinted down the dune, bounding straight for the flag. Thousands of soldiers turned to look at the strange, red fox rushing across the sand.

"I didn't have a chance to tell him," Malachi said. "Whenever someone walks between the two armies, that triggers them into action."

Sure enough, just when Red was squarely between the two armies, someone shouted, "CHARGE!"

Then someone on the other side bellowed, "CHARGE!"

The two sides swarmed down the dunes—with Red caught in the middle.

As the two armies closed in on each other, soldiers began firing their musical instruments, blasting streams of sand from tubas and trombones. The instruments made off-tune sounds as they shot out sand—tons of it flying in every direction.

"Okay, now I see why they're called sandblasters," said Emily.

Red vanished in a massive cloud of swirling sand as the two armies crashed into each other.

"You're up," Malachi said, turning to Aiden. "Time for you to be a hero."

"Hop on my back," Melchior said, and Aiden looked at Malachi to see if it was okay.

When Malachi nodded, they disconnected Melchior's sled, which carried the Sand Box. Then Aiden took off his backpack, leaped onto the camel, and shouted, "Charge!" Together, they raced down the dune toward the armies below. Aiden and Melchior were an army of two versus thousands.

# INTO THE STORM

Aiden still couldn't believe the soldiers were firing streams of sand from their trombones, tubas, and trumpets. It was weird, but also kind of cool. If his trumpet back at home had shot sand, maybe he'd still be playing it. Even the piccolo players fired thin streams of sand, like shooting darts from a blowgun. Every so often, the trumpet cannons would fire, sending a huge ball of sand into a cluster of soldiers, knocking them flat and burying them.

The sand flew every which way, and it was so thick that Aiden could no longer see the flag…or Red.

In moments, they were in the heart of the madness—without a way to defend themselves. In the whirling sand, Aiden could see only a few feet to either side. Soldiers on both sides fired on them. When he turned to his left, a clump of sand hit him squarely in the face, nearly knocking him off of Melchior's back.

His ears were ringing, and he spit out sand.

"You all right?" Melchior asked.

"I'm fine. But I don't see how we're going to find the flag in this craziness. Are you still going in the right direction?"

"To be honest…I have no idea," Melchior said. "I was hoping you did."

"Incoming!" someone shouted.

Aiden looked up to see a huge ball of sand, probably three feet in diameter, arching across the sky and falling right toward them. Melchior spurred forward just in time. The sand cannonball landed with a WHOOOMP directly behind them, burying one of the soldiers.

"Do you hear that?" Aiden asked.

"Hear what?"

"A drum. I don't remember seeing any soldiers carrying drums, but I hear it. Do you?"

"I do," said Melchior. "When soldiers play drums in battle, they're usually sending signals. Do you think the snare drum is sending a signal?"

Aiden shot up straight in the saddle. "What did you just call the drum?"

"A snare drum. The kind of drums soldiers carry into battle."

The words slowly sunk in. "Malachi told me to be snared by prayer."

The camel gave that some thought. "I think he means you should start praying."

"But maybe he also wants me to follow the sound of the snare drum."

"Probably you should do both. Start praying, and I'll try to follow the sound."

"Dear Lord…" Aiden began, but then he stopped.

"What're you waiting for?" Melchior said. "The drum is sounding fainter."

But Aiden was out of practice in prayer. After "Dear Lord," what do you say?

"Prayer is just talking to God. Just talk, like you would with me," said Melchior.

"All right, here goes…" Aiden was so distracted by the battle raging everywhere that he couldn't think straight.

"I can't hear the drum any longer!" Melchior said. "Start praying!"

Finally, he sputtered to a start. "Hello, God, this is Aiden. We could really use your help about now. We're caught in a battle with sand flying all around, and we can't see hardly a thing, let alone the flag."

He paused. Off in the distance, the drum began playing again, even louder than before.

"Dear Jesus, also help us to find Red. He got caught in the middle of this battle, and I'm afraid he's buried somewhere."

The drumbeat picked up, increasing in volume. It seemed to be coming from their right.

"Lord, I know I haven't talked to you much these days, and I'm really sorry. I would say I've been too busy, but you know that's not true. We've been stuck inside because of this virus thing. You'd think I'd have tons of time to talk with you."

"We're getting closer!" said Melchior. "Keep it up, Aiden!"

"And speaking of the virus, I also pray for our country—and the world. It's such a mess. Things seem to be crumbling apart, and we need you."

The drumbeat picked up pace, growing ever louder.

"I also thank you, Lord, for bringing us to Redvale again—and for bringing us back together with friends like Melchior."

As Melchior turned to the left, following the sound of the drum, the battle increased in intensity. The flying sand was so thick that Aiden couldn't see but a few feet in front of him. The off-tune tubas sounded like fog-horn blasts.

Aiden began to shout his prayer. "Lord, please help Red, wherever he is. Please lead us to the flag. PLEASE HELP US!"

Suddenly, the veil of sand parted, like opening a curtain. There, not far away, was the flag! The flag wasn't being guarded, so this was their chance to snatch the key. They were going to make it! He was going to succeed. Then...

"Help me!" called a familiar voice.

Aiden shot a look to his left and saw Red, buried in sand up to his shoulders. Even worse, three soldiers were preparing to fire their sandblasters at the little fox. They aimed their trumpets and let loose with a *WHOOOOSH* of sand.

Red was completely buried. He was gone. Vanished.

# CAPTURE THE KEY

Aiden saw his chance to grab the key, while the flag was still unguarded. He had to act fast. On the other hand, he couldn't just ignore Red. The little fox was buried! He needed Aiden's help now! What if Red couldn't breathe underneath all of that sand? If Aiden went for the key, would he doom his friend?

"What do we do?" Melchior said.

Aiden groaned at the misery of this decision. He had to get the key. Isabella succeeded in her mission. If he failed because of Red...

He was confused and angry.

"Lead me to Red!" Aiden said, tugging on Melchior's reins. "Quickly!"

Melchior wheeled around. When they reached the spot where Red had disappeared, Aiden leaped from the camel's back and began digging frantically.

"Please Lord, let Red be safe! Help me find him!"

Melchior used his big feet to help dig, but where was Red? Why weren't they finding him? How deep was he buried?

"What are you looking for?" came a voice from behind. "Can I help?"

"I'm trying to save my friend, Red!"

"Awwww, that's so nice of you, Aiden. But you're digging in the wrong pile of sand. I was buried back here. But it's the thought that counts."

Aiden whirled around. Red was standing right behind them, calmly watching them dig. Aiden wrapped the fox in a huge hug. "I'm so happy you're safe!"

"So am I. But don't you think we need to be grabbing that key?" Red motioned toward the flag.

"Uh…That's going to be a problem," Melchior said.

By this time, soldiers were guarding the flag, and they aimed a trumpet cannon directly at them.

"Oh no you don't!" Aiden shouted, hopping onto Melchior's back. "Charge!"

The camel took off, hurtling straight for the flag and the cannon. If they fired that thing, it was going to really hurt, Aiden thought.

"Ready! Aim!" the soldiers shouted.

Melchior was in a full sprint now, closing in on the flag—and the cannon.

"Fire!"

*BA-BOOOOM!*

Aiden braced himself for the crushing blow of a sand cannonball. But he didn't feel a thing. Red had run ahead, and he had pushed the cannon upward just before it went off. The sand cannonball flew inches above Aiden's head, ruffling his hair as it whipped past.

With Melchior in full gallop, Aiden leaned down as they raced toward flag, soldiers scattering in their path. Leaning over even more, he snagged the key as they rushed past the flag—and then he lost his balance and tumbled off. Aiden did somersaults down the dune, head over heels, terrified that the key had been flung out of his hand.

"Please, Lord, I pray I didn't lose the key," he said, as he lay sprawled on the ground. He gasped for breath and slowly sat up. Then he opened his clenched fist. The key was gone!

"Looking for this?" said Red, standing beside him. "The key flew from your hand, but I'm a pretty good catch if I have to say so myself."

Red had the key in his paw.

Meanwhile, all had gone silent. The moment they snagged the key, the fighting stopped. Shaking the sand from his hair, Aiden got to his feet. All of the soldiers were standing around, looking stunned, as if they had just awakened from a dream.

They stood in a daze for a good minute, staring at the musical instruments in their hands, as if they didn't know what to do with them. Suddenly, one of the soldiers in red and one of the soldiers in green put the trumpets to their lips—and they began to play together. It was a beautiful melody, and it carried across the vast desert. Then all of the other soldiers remembered what their instruments were made to do, and they too began to play. A great chorus rang to the heavens.

Aiden put Red on his shoulders, as Melchior, Malachi, and his sisters came running up to them, big smiles all around. They listened in awe to the music. And when the playing died down, one of the trumpeters walked directly up to Aiden.

"Thank you for bringing our music back to life," the soldier said to Aiden. "Here. I'd like to give you this."

The soldier held out his trumpet. Aiden was flabbergasted.

"Oh, I couldn't take your trumpet. You need it."

"I think you need it more than I do," the musician said. "I have a hunch it's going to come in handy."

"Are you sure?"

"I couldn't be more sure."

Aiden took the trumpet and ran his hand across the polished brass. Then he raised the trumpet to his mouth and played. He never sounded better in his life.

# TO BE CONTINUED ON PAGE 176.

TO BE CONTINUED ON PAGE 176.

# DAY 20

## A STEP IN THE RIGHT DIRECTION

### TREASURE HUNTING

Today, there are thousands of treasure hunters all around the world, and not a single one of them has a parrot perched on their shoulder or an eye patch. Most probably wear jeans and a T-shirt.

They're called "geocachers." It all started back in 2000, when a man from Portland, Oregon, decided to partially bury a five-gallon bucket about one mile from his house. Inside the bucket was a "treasure" of videos, books, software, money, a can of beans, and a slingshot. The goal was for people to locate this treasure using their GPS—global positioning system.

Since then, geocaching has become a worldwide craze. Treasures are hidden at GPS coordinates all over the world. For instance, the coordinates might look something like this:

## 28.822133, -81.622633

People plug those coordinates into their phone or GPS device and off they go! The coordinates get them close to the treasure—but not to the exact spot. They still have to do some searching.

Life is a lot like a treasure hunt. We're constantly looking for directions in life. We wonder… What should I be when I grow up? Where should I live? Who should I marry?

Wouldn't it be great if we had a GPS in our pocket that could give us instant directions? But life doesn't work that way. To find our way in life, we have prayer on our side. You might even call prayer a GPS of a different sort—a God Positioning System.

# RECALCULATING...

People use GPS systems to find lost items, like keys or phones. GPS can give you directions to far-off cities. It has even been used to track down poachers who are trying to kill elephants for their tusks.

But GPS is not perfect. One person almost drove off a cliff because he was following GPS. Another person drove 900 miles in the wrong direction because her GPS told her to go that way. So, even the world's best system for giving directions can send us the wrong way.

Again, it's just like life. The world is constantly trying to send us directions, telling us what we should be and how we should live. For instance…

- Advertisements tell us we desperately need to buy the latest thing.
- A jingle on the radio tells us to eat there, look this way, talk like him, think like her…
- A billboard tells us to visit certain places.
- Fast-food ads tell us we're really, really hungry.

Like GPS, some of these messages send us in the right direction. But some of them send us the wrong way or may even try to control us.

So where do you go? Who do you follow?

## DESTINATION: JESUS
If you want to head in the right direction, follow Jesus.

God's plan is to redeem the world and put things right. In other words, this present world is not our final destination. The Bible says we're foreigners and exiles in the world; some translations even call us aliens (but not the kind that arrive in spaceships).

The Bible calls us to be different from the world. Therefore, we need directions to find our true home, and we get that from Jesus.

> **"Friends, this world is not your home, so don't make yourselves cozy in it. Don't indulge your ego at the expense of your soul. Live an exemplary life among the natives so that your actions will refute their prejudices. Then they'll be won over to God's side and be there to join in the celebration when he arrives." 1 Peter 2:11-12 (*The Message*)**

When we find ourselves in a confusing world, not knowing what to do or which way to go, then go to God. Praying to God gives you direction in a confusing world. He promises that if we ask, He'll lead you to Himself, which is the greatest treasure you can ever seek. He'll lead you to your true home.

# TARGET PRACTICE

We're going to spend this week talking about prayer. Let's begin by checking how much you Pause to Pray in your life. Below are three questions and three targets. Color the target ring that connects to your answer for each question.

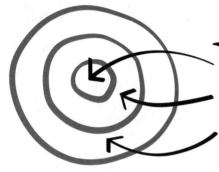

## HOW OFTEN DO YOU PRAY?

EVERY DAY (6-7 TIMES PER WEEK)

SOMETIMES (2-5 TIMES PER WEEK)

ALMOST NEVER (0-1 TIMES PER WEEK)

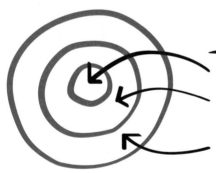

## WHEN YOU PRAY, HOW OFTEN DO YOU KNOW GOD HEARS YOU?

ALWAYS!

SOMETIMES, I THINK.

NEVER. I DON'T KNOW IF HE HEARS ME OR NOT.

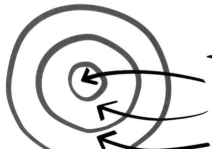

## HOW OFTEN DO YOU PRAY WITH YOUR FAMILY?

ALWAYS

SOMETIMES

NEVER

# DAY 21

## FIRST RESPONSE OR LAST RESORT?

### DISSECTING YOUR DAY

"Dissection" is when you take something apart, like a clock, to find out how it works. We're going to "dissect" your typical day to find out what makes it tick. For starters, what is the very first thing you did this morning after brushing your teeth and going to the bathroom? Write it out below or draw a picture of what you did.

Next, write down what a typical day for you is like. What do you do throughout the day?

# MY TYPICAL DAY

**EARLY MORNING** (7 to 9 a.m.) _____

_____

**MID-MORNING** (10 to 11 a.m.) _____

_____

**NOON HOUR** _____

_____

**EARLY AFTERNOON** (1 to 3 p.m.) _____

_____

**LATE AFTERNOON** (4 to 5 p.m.) _____

_____

**EARLY EVENING** (6 to 7 p.m.) _____

_____

**LATE EVENING** (8 to 9 p.m.) _____

_____

**BEDTIME ROUTINE** (note the time you go to sleep) _____

_____

# OLD HABITS, NEW HABITS

Habits are things we do regularly, often without thinking, such as flossing our teeth or exercising. Habits allow our brain to focus on learning new things. The brain doesn't have to think about the things we already know how to do—our old habits. This frees up our mind to concentrate on new things.

For example, when you were one year old and learning to walk, you had to spend a lot of time working on it. You had to practice your balance, moving one foot forward and then the other. You had to watch closely where you were going, noticing when the floor changed from carpet to tile. You also had to think about how far you were from your destination and how easy it was going to be to reach it.

Today, you don't have to think about walking at all, unless you're trying to learn something new, like walking a tightrope or crossing dangerous "slowsand" on a balance beam. You can even do other things while walking, like eat an ice cream cone.

You have hundreds of habits you do every day. So did Jesus. But He had one habit that He did first thing in the morning. He prayed.

## HIT THE PAUSE BUTTON

Jesus prayed first thing in the morning. By pausing for prayer right away in the morning, Jesus showed people that prayer was important. It was so important that He did it before anything else in His day.

**"Very early in the morning, while it was still dark, Jesus got up, left the house and went off to a solitary place, where he prayed." Mark 1:35**

Also, note that Jesus didn't pray just once and He was done for the day. He paused to pray ALL THE TIME. The famous Underground Railroad leader, Harriet Tubman, prayed all the time by connecting her prayers to what she was doing. When she was cleaning something, she asked Jesus to clean her heart. When she was sweeping, she asked the Lord to sweep the sins from her life.

# ALONE TIME

Jesus was very busy, always surrounded by lots of people seeking to be healed. So when Jesus was alone, He had to choose to be alone. **"But Jesus often withdrew to lonely places and prayed,"** says Luke 5:16.

Circle the words "withdrew" and "lonely" in the verse from Luke above. Then circle the word "solitary" in the verse from Mark at the beginning of the "Hit the Pause Button" section. Notice anything similar about these words?

- **SOLITARY**—being alone

- **WITHDREW**—to remove or take away something from a particular place

- **LONELY**—without companions, solitary

As you can see, "lonely" doesn't mean "sad" in this verse. It means being somewhere without anyone else around. So, Jesus prayed often, more than once a day, and He prayed in places where He could be alone.

We could learn a lot from His prayer habits.

# PRAYER: THE V.I.T. OF LIFE

To Pause to Pray like Jesus, aim for two goals:

**①** **PRAY FIRST.**

**②** **PRAY OFTEN.**

When we're nervous before a game, excited about eating our favorite meal, sad about something, or proud about scoring a goal, Pause to Pray. Make it a VIT in your day—a Very Important Thing! Make it the first thing you do, not a last resort.

If you do that, prayer will be a habit, something that comes naturally, like walking.

As Abraham Lincoln said, "I have been driven many times upon my knees by the overwhelming conviction that I had nowhere else to go. My own wisdom, and that of all about me, seemed insufficient for the day."

# CHALLENGE

Corrie Ten Boom was a Dutch woman who hid Jews when the Nazis were hunting them during World War II. She loved Jesus, and she once said that we shouldn't pray only when we feel like it. "Have an appointment with the Lord and keep it," she said. "A man is powerful on his knees."

Look back on the Typical Day that you filled in at the beginning of this chapter. Use a colored pen or marker to draw "pause signs" next to the times when you want to Pause to Pray.

Also, set an alarm on your device or on your Google Home or have a parent set an alarm on his or her phone. The alarms remind you to Pause to Pray.

# RED ALERT!

The Bible talks about praying "in the name of Jesus." (John 14:13-14) These are not magic words we tag at the end of prayers. To pray in Jesus's name means we seek His will. We obey His will.

# DAY 22

## HOW YOU SHOULD PRAY

### JUST PRAY IT

Below are some famous slogans, but they're missing key words. Fill in the blanks
or quiz your mom and dad or friend and see how well they do.

JUST _____ IT. (NIKE)

THE QUICKER _____ _____. (BOUNTY)

AMERICA RUNS _____ _____. (DUNKIN DONUTS)

_____ LOVIN' _____. (MCDONALDS)

LIKE A GOOD _____ _____ _____ IS THERE.
(STATE FARM INSURANCE)

Slogans are short, catchy phrases used to help people remember a business. The
word "slogan" comes from Scotland, and it means "army" (slaugh) and "shout"
(gairn). When people are working for a common goal, an "army shout" gets
everyone together. It makes you feel like you're on the same team.

When Jesus taught His disciples, He wanted them to know they were all on the same mission, on the same team, or in the same army. Let's look at how He did that.

## GOD'S ARMY SHOUT

When Christians say the Lord's Prayer, it's like an "army shout" that binds us all together. In the Lord's Prayer below, circle the words OUR, US, and WE.

> **"Our Father in heaven, hallowed be your name, your kingdom come, your will be done, on earth as it is in heaven. Give us today our daily bread. And forgive us our debts, as we also have forgiven our debtors. And lead us not into temptation, but deliver us from the evil one."** **Matthew 6:9-13**

When you say this prayer, it reminds us we're not alone. We're part of a team, or an army. Say this prayer out loud, even like a shout! It should fill you with excitement!

According to one tradition, when a scribe was copying the Lord's Prayer hundreds and hundreds of years ago, he got so excited that he wrote to the side: "For thine is the kingdom, and the power, and the glory, forever. Amen!" Later, people thought his words were actually part of the prayer. So, even though those words are not in the Bible, it's how many of us end the Lord's Prayer today when we say it out loud.

It's a wonderful ending to our Lord's "army shout."

## THE MODEL PRAYER

Even though the Lord's Prayer is an amazing prayer, sometimes we say it at church without really thinking about the words. Have you ever noticed that? The next time you say the Lord's Prayer, *really think* about every sentence, every word. Let it fill you up.

"The Lord's Prayer is the model prayer," says the *People's Bible Commentary*. "It is a lesson on how to pray and what to pray for."

According to this commentary, the Lord's Prayer covers all of our needs of body and soul. It's a prayer for our fellow Christians and for millions of people who do not know the Lord Jesus. It's a prayer for every occasion. It "puts first things first, but leaves nothing out."

## CHALLENGE

We don't always pray perfectly. We don't always use the right words or pray for the right reasons. But Jesus doesn't ask for perfect prayers. He wants us to come to God with our prayers at any time. He welcomes us with open arms.

## RED ALERT!

Jewish people often thought of sins as "debts." A debt is when you owe somebody something, such as money. When somebody forgives your debt, you don't have to pay back the money. You're set free. Forgiveness sets us free of our sins.

Let's look at each section of the Lord's Prayer to find out what it means. Then you can personalize it by putting it in your own words.

| LORD'S PRAYER | WHAT IT MEANS | MY PRAYER |
| --- | --- | --- |
| Our Father in heaven | We call God "Father" because we're His children. We have a connection that no one can break. | _____ |
| Hallowed be your name | God's name is holy. We praise you and give you honor. | _____ |
| Your kingdom come, your will be done on earth as it is in heaven. | We want to follow God and do what He asks us to do. | _____ |
| Give us today our daily bread. | We trust that God will take care of us. | _____ |
| Forgive us our debts, as we have also forgiven our debtors. | Because we're sure that Jesus forgives all of our sins, we can can forgive others when they hurt us. | _____ |
| And lead us not into temptation | God will help us to follow and obey Him. | _____ |
| But deliver us from the evil one. | God can keep evil from hurting us. | _____ |
| For yours is the kingdom, and the power, and the glory forever. Amen. | God has defeated the enemy. We are in His army, but God has already won the battle for us— the battle over sin. | _____ |

# DAY 23

## PRACTICE PRAYER

---

## PARENT TALK

Sometimes, it seems as if parents have a secret language all their own. Parents across the country say the same kinds of things to their kids, over and over. Color in the bubbles of the phrases you've heard an adult say:

BE QUIET SO I CAN HEAR MYSELF THINK!

STOP CLIMBING THE WALLS.

IF YOU KEEP MAKING THAT FACE, IT WILL FREEZE THAT WAY!

ONE DAY YOU'LL THANK ME.

I'M NOT ASKING, I'M TELLING.

BECAUSE I SAID SO, THAT'S WHY.

IF YOU ACT LIKE A CHILD, I WILL TREAT YOU LIKE ONE.

Another popular phrase that adults often say is "practice makes perfect." Practice means repeating the same motion, action, song, or idea over and over and over. It's not easy, and to be honest it can be pretty boring. But it's very important. The writer Malcolm Gladwell said that to become an expert at something, you have to do it for roughly 10,000 hours! That's eight hours a day, five days a week, for five years. This means you might be an expert at going to school by now, so that's cool! (Or maybe not.)

It's difficult to practice for one hour, let alone 10,000! What's something you have had to practice?

_____

_____

# PRACTICE AND PERFECTION

No athlete reaches the Olympic games without practicing. Many of them had to do schoolwork at their gym or practice facility on breaks because they spent eight hours or more per day practicing—probably trying to reach those 10,000 hours.

But practice does NOT make perfect. If you watch the Olympics, you'll see that only one person gets the gold medal, and even the winner can't say he or she is "perfect" in a sport. "Practice makes better," but we aren't perfect.

Only one perfect person lived on this planet, and that was Jesus. He spent a lot of time pausing for prayer. So He was the perfect example of how we should pray.

If you want to become better at prayer, you have to get started. The best way to learn to pray is by just simply praying.

Bow your head and talk to Jesus. He's listening. That's all prayer is—communicating with God. There's not a right way or wrong way to pray. Hebrews 4:16 says, **"Let us then approach God's throne with confidence, so that we may receive mercy and find grace to help us in our time of need."**

Some people are very good at praying. Maybe they Pause to Pray twenty times in a day, and maybe they speak the most beautiful prayers. That's wonderful, but remember: all of that practice will not make them perfect.

Jesus came to earth to be perfect for us when we can't be perfect. **"For by one sacrifice he has made perfect forever those who are being made holy." Hebrews 10:14.** This means that when He died and rose to life victorious, He made you perfect in God's eyes.

Practice doesn't make perfect. Jesus makes perfect.

# EYES ON GOD

The Jewish people prayed three times a day—at 9 a.m., noon, and 3 p.m. Praying regularly like that is wonderful, but Jesus noticed one big problem. Some people would stand in the middle of the street or busy market and pray loudly for all to hear. They weren't trying to show how great God is. They wanted to show how great they are.

Remember, the focus of prayer is on God. All eyes should go to Him, not on you. Another thing the Bible says is to **"pray continually" 1 Thessalonians 5:17.** But that's pretty confusing. Pray continually? Like, never stopping? Not even to sleep? Or eat? No one can do that!

When the Bible says "continually," it means we should pray often and faithfully.

## CHALLENGE

One way to practice prayer is to say the prayers of those who have come before us. Amazingly, many of the Psalms are prayers, including Psalm 23. Read through Psalm 23 today. As you're reading, stop after each verse and talk to God about that verse.

# RED ALERT!

There are many kinds of Psalms. There are hymns, or songs of praise. There are wisdom Psalms and thanksgiving Psalms. There are royal psalms you sing to a King. There are also "laments"—when you cry out to God in difficult times.

# DAY 24

## PAUSE FOR PRAISE

### PRESENTS AND PRAISE

Imagine the greatest gift in the world. This might be a gift you actually received, or something you'd really, really like to get. In the gift box below, draw this present—or write it down.

WHAT DOES THIS PRESENT DO? WHAT'S IT FOR?

_____

HOW DOES THIS GIFT MAKE YOUR LIFE BETTER?

_____

When we receive a fabulous gift, one of the first things we think is, "I've got to tell someone about it!" Telling others is a big part of the fun!

This is what praise is all about. It's telling someone about the Lord. That's why praise is one of the most powerful prayers we can say.

# THE PRAISE PRAYER

The Lord's Prayer begins with praise: **"Our Father who art in heaven, hallowed be your name."**

*"Hallowed"* is not a word we commonly use, so it can be difficult to understand. But hallowed means "to make holy or to honor." So, the Lord's Prayer begins by honoring God's holy name—by praising His name.

God has many names in the Bible. Circle the ones you've heard before.

**Almighty** (Revelation 1:8)

**Alpha and Omega** (Revelation 1:8)

**Author of Life** (Acts 3:15)

**Bread of Life** (John 6:35, 48)

**Carpenter** (Mark 6:3)

**Chief Cornerstone** (Ephesians 2:20)

**Christ** (Matthew 1:16, ESV)

**Comforter** (Jeremiah 8:18)

**Everlasting Father** (Isaiah 9:6)

**Foundation** (Isaiah 28:16)

**High Priest** (Hebrews 3:1)

**Holy One** (Isaiah 1:4)

**Immanuel** (Matthew 1:23)

**Jesus** (Matthew 1:21)

**King of Kings** (1 Timothy 6:15)

**Lamb of God** (John 1:29)

**Light of the World** (John 8:12)

**Lion of the Tribe of Judah** (Revelation 5:5)

**Lord of Lords** (1 Timothy 6:15)

**Messiah** (Matthew 1:16)

**Mighty God** (Isaiah 9:6)

**Morning Star** (2 Peter 1:19)

**Prince of Peace** (Isaiah 9:6)

**Redeemer** (Isaiah 41:14)

**Rock** (Deuteronomy 32:4)

**Root of David** (Revelation 5:5, 22:16)

**Shepherd** (1 Peter 2:25)

**Teacher** (John 3:2)

**Vine** (John 15:1)

**Wonderful Counselor** (Isaiah 9:6)

There is power in saying God's name out loud. **"God's name is a place of protection—good people can run there and be safe,"** says Proverbs 18:10 (*The Message*).

# WE'RE MADE TO PRAISE

We praise God's name through both our words and our actions. But God doesn't want us to praise Him because He needs it. God asks us to praise Him because WE need it. Praising God helps us to love Him in stronger and better ways. For example…

● Praising God can make us less worried or scared because we remember He is our Lion, the Almighty, and the Prince of Peace.

● Praising God can help us trust God to take care of us because He is our Bread of Life, a Good Shepherd, and our Comforter.

● Praising God can help us when we're confused because He is our Teacher, King of Kings, High Priest, and Wonderful Counselor.

If you're afraid of the dark, which name of God would you use to call on Him?

_____

_____

## HOW DO WE PRAISE GOD?

We can praise God by:

- Describing the greatness of God. Each of His names tells us something about Him.

- Talking about what He has done for us and knowing what He will do in the future. The Bible describes some incredible things God has done throughout history.

- Seeing how our life is different because of God. You are a child of God. Without God, we are left dead in our sins.

**"As for you, you were dead in your transgressions and sins,"** says Ephesians 2:1. But God did not leave us this way. He had a rescue plan!

## THE ULTIMATE GIFT

Earlier, you described a pretty cool gift. But God has given us an even greater gift. He gave His own Son to die for us. Jesus took your place because He loves you, and He was the only one who could save you.

God entered the world to save the world. His love is higher, bigger, and more marvelous than any gift you could ever unwrap. He loved you before you could say one peep of praise.

We don't praise God to make Him happy with us or to get something from Him. We praise Him because we've already been given EVERYTHING in Jesus.

Now, that's something to shout about!

# CHALLENGE

Praise God in three different ways today. Focus on who He is, what He has done throughout history, and how He makes your life better.

## PICK YOUR FAVORITE NAME FOR GOD.

Look up the Bible verse and write it here:

## WHAT HAS GOD DONE?

Write or draw something that you remember God did in the Bible.

## HOW HAS GOD MADE YOUR LIFE BETTER?

MAKE UP YOUR OWN NAME
FOR GOD AND WRITE IT INSIDE
THE TREASURE CHEST.

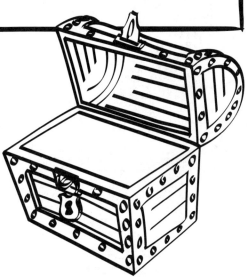

# RED ALERT!

Jesus is called the Lamb of God because He died for our sins, just as Jewish people used to sacrifice lambs in the Temple for sins. Jesus died on the cross at the ninth hour (3 p.m.). This was the exact same time that a lamb was being sacrificed in the Temple.

# DAY 25

## PRAYER CHANGES THINGS

### ALADDIN'S WISHES

In the story of Aladdin, a young street urchin stumbles upon a magic lamp and discovers a powerful, fun-loving genie inside. When Aladdin rubs the lamp, the genie pops out and grants him three wishes.

Sometimes, we treat God like He too is a genie in a lamp. We pray only when we're in trouble. When we pray, we only ask Him for things we need. We forget to praise or thank Him for what we already have.

God also isn't a vending machine. We can't put in a prayer, like a quarter in a vending machine, and expect our wish to pop out.

God controls everything in the universe, and He knows everything that's going to happen. But does that mean He is just a good luck charm or wish granter? For instance, if we don't want our family to move, or if we want the weather to change so our tournament isn't rained out, can our prayers change these things?

That was the question faced by a girl named Maren.

# MAREN'S PRAYER

Maren's dad got a new job in a new city, and their family was packing to move. But Maren didn't want to go. She liked her school and loved her bedroom. She had fun with her friends and knew everyone in Sunday School class. Moving meant she would have to start all over. She'd be the new girl, and everything would be different and scary.

Maren learned all about prayer at church. So she decided to ask God that her family wouldn't move. She prayed every day. She knew that God could make a job open up for her dad in town, allowing them to stay. But after praying every day for two weeks, Maren's family moved. Maren said goodbye to all of her friends and the familiar places she loved. She packed up all of the stuff from her beautiful bedroom and sat on the backyard tire swing one last time, feeling sad.

Later, as their car pulled out of the driveway, she fought back tears. "Where was God?" she wondered. "Why weren't my prayers answered?"

# PRAYERS THAT CHANGED THINGS

We'll get back to Maren's important questions. But first let's look at ways that prayer in the Bible changed God's mind.

- The Israelites had grumbling attitudes after they escaped from Egypt and wanted to rebel against Moses. When God said a plague was going to strike the rebellious Israelites, Moses asked that they be spared. Because of Moses, God changed His mind and had mercy on them. (Numbers 14:1-20)

- The prophet Isaiah told Hezekiah that the Lord said he was going to die. But Hezekiah, who was sick, prayed to God, and the Lord lengthened his life by fifteen years. (Isaiah 38:1-4)

● After Jonah told the Ninevites that God was going to destroy them, the people of Nineveh repented. Then God changed His mind and had mercy on Nineveh. (Jonah 3)

Every time we see God changing His mind, it's always for our benefit. It's always a change toward grace and kindness and away from rightful punishment. So, if you want God to change something, remember that He moves toward grace.

Our prayers matter. Prayer can change situations. It also changes us. As it says in James 5:16b, **"The prayer of a righteous person is powerful and effective."**

## GOD'S PLAN IS UNCHANGING

God sometimes changes His mind about a specific thing. But His will and His plan never changes. God's plan is to save everyone in the world from sin, and He wants to restore the earth to what it once was before sin entered Eden. This plan has never changed. It's a promise that cannot be broken. No matter what happens, God will keep His end of the deal.

In addition, Jesus said this promise is for ALL people. **"This righteousness is given through faith in Jesus Christ to all who believe." Romans 3:22a**

## MAREN'S LESSONS

Maren eventually learned that God's will is bigger than her own wishes. At her new home, she had a difficult time. For a couple of years, she had a hard time making new friends. But she turned to God and learned things she never would've learned if things had been easy. God was with her, even in the hard times.

After a couple of extremely difficult years, she made a new best friend, Katy, who had horses at her house in the country. Because of her friendship with Katy, Maren discovered that she loved horses and wanted to become a veterinarian. Later, she even went to college so she could work with horses. God was with her in the good times too.

Maren learned that prayer is a lot more complicated than just getting what you want. She experienced both the good and the bad, and she learned that God had a plan for her through it all. We cannot see the future, but God can. He doesn't promise a perfect life. He promises His presence. Sometimes, it can seem like He's not listening or doesn't care about us, but He does.

Pray big. Pray bold. God is listening to us. He's also speaking to us.

# CHALLENGE

Instead of three wishes, write down three big prayer requests. After you pray for them, thank God that He knows what's best for you.

**1** _____

**2** _____

**3** _____

# DAY 26

## PERSISTENT PRAYER

---

### I WANT IT NOW!

We don't like to wait for things.

Look at the brand names below and write down what you used these services
to get. Maybe you were trying to find information, or maybe you were ordering
food. Write down how long it took for you to get something from these services.
Finally, if you got something quickly, put a checkmark next to the brand name.

| | WHAT I GOT | HOW LONG IT TOOK |
|---|---|---|
| ☐ GOOGLE/SIRI/ALEXA | | |
| ☐ TV/MOVIE STREAMING (Netflix, Hulu, Amazon Prime) | | |
| ☐ GROCERY DELIVERY | | |
| ☐ PIZZA DELIVERY | | |
| ☐ OTHER FOOD DELIVERY (postmates, grubhub, uber eats, doordash) | | |
| ☐ AMAZON, TARGET, OR WALMART DELIVERY | | |
| ☐ _____ | | |

People go to these companies because speed sells. Years ago, people had to wait a whole week for the new episode of a TV show. But now you can stream an entire season at once. When you text a friend, you probably expect him or her to answer right away. We're used to getting things NOW.

But not everything in life comes quickly—and that includes answers to prayer. Some prayers are answered quickly. But others are not.

# A PRAYER PARABLE

Jesus talked about how answers to prayer sometimes don't come as fast as we want. He illustrated this in a famous parable. Jesus told the disciples a story showing that it was necessary for them to pray consistently and never quit. He said...

> "There was once a judge in some city who never gave God a thought and cared nothing for people. A widow in that city kept after him: 'My rights are being violated. Protect me!'

> "He never gave her the time of day. But after this went on and on he said to himself, 'I care nothing what God thinks, even less what people think. But because this widow won't quit badgering me, I'd better do something and see that she gets justice—otherwise I'm going to end up beaten black-and-blue by her pounding.'"

> **Then the Master said,** "Do you hear what that judge, corrupt as he is, is saying? So what makes you think God won't step in and work justice for his chosen people, who continue to cry out for help? Won't he stick up

for them? I assure you, he will. He will not drag his feet. But how much of that kind of persistent faith will the Son of Man find on the earth when he returns?" **Luke 18:1-8 (*The Message*)**

Who do you think Jesus was comparing the judge to in the story? Who is the widow supposed to be? Write your answers below.

THE JUDGE: _____

THE WIDOW: _____

Hold on a second! The parable said the judge didn't care about people. It even said he didn't care about God. This guy sounds like a regular Scrooge. So why would Jesus compare him to God?

Jesus wasn't trying to say God is like a grumpy, old judge. He was trying to show that if a mean judge could show kindness to a widow who didn't give up, then a loving, caring God will listen. A loving God will do everything He can to give His children what we faithfully ask for.

That widow prayed with persistence, which means not giving up. Persistent prayer is when we pray over and over and over and over and over and over for the same thing. It's when we have faith that what we're praying for is part of God's will.

Persistent prayer is powerful.

# HOW MUCH LONGER, LORD?

Did you notice how Jesus ended the parable? Write down the last sentence of the parable below. (Hint: He ended with a question.)

_____

_____

Another way to put this question is: "Who will not give up? Who will keep praying when things get hard?" Is there something you prayed for that you gave up on? If you hadn't given up on that prayer, could things be different? It's possible, depending on what you prayed for, of course.

Jesus never gives up on us. So don't give up on Him.

# CHALLENGE

What prayer have you given up on? Pray for that today.

Write down something that you or someone else prayed about for years and years before God moved.

_____

_____

_____

_____

_____

DAYS

# 27-33

OF THE 40 DAY CHALLENGE

KEYSTONE HABIT 4:

# STOP SOLIT

FOR
UDE

# THE SANDS OF REDVALE

## PART 5

Emily stared in amazement as the musicians marched up and down the sand dunes, playing music that soared. Her brother had done a wonder. When Aiden retrieved the key, the two enemy armies suddenly became one unified marching band.

"Tremendous job," Malachi said to Aiden.

"I couldn't have done it without Red and Melchior."

"So true," said Red, before launching into a long retelling of their entire adventure, mostly focusing on his exploits. When Red finally finished talking, all three kids (plus Red) put their hands (and paw) together to insert the Prayer Key into the Sand Box.

CLICK! Like the other keys, it fit perfectly. Three keys down. Two to go.

"And what about this?" Aiden said, pointing at the latest flag. It had the picture of a ship on it with a cross on the main sail. "What's this flag all about?"

"It's the flag of the disciple Jude," Malachi said. "The flag has a ship on it because Jude traveled the world as a missionary."

"And prayer was the wind in his sails," Melchior added. "Prayer can carry you anywhere."

"So what's next?" Red said. "Do I get to retrieve the next key? Do I?"

"Patience," Malachi said. "The next key is Emily's to find."

Red crossed his arms and scowled.

"Don't worry, Red, maybe you can help me," said Emily, putting an arm around the fox.

"I'm afraid that's not possible," Malachi said. "The next key is the Solitude Key, and you must retrieve it alone, Emily."

"Figures," said Red.

It didn't seem fair, Emily thought. Why should Aiden get help from both Red and Melchior, while she has to do her mission completely alone?

Both Emily and Red grumbled to themselves as the caravan began the slow trek deeper into the desert. They came across two more flags in short order. The flag of James, the son of Alphaeus, carried the picture of two rocks, because James was stoned to death. The flag of Simon the Zealot displayed a fish on top of a Bible because, like the other disciples, he was a fisher of men.

Lost in her thoughts, Emily became increasingly worried about the mission she would soon face. Her worries only multiplied when they stopped for lunch.

"No! It can't be!" Emily shouted.

All eyes snapped in her direction as she pulled a cheese sandwich from their sack of supplies. The sandwich had literally become a SANDwich! Her two slices of bread had transformed to sand, and so had most of the cheese. It crumbled in her hands.

"We're going to have to hike on empty stomachs," Malachi said. "We better pick up the pace. Time is not on our side."

For Emily, it didn't seem as if *anything* was on their side.

# THE MUSTARD SEED

"I still don't understand," said Emily, slipping up beside Malachi when the caravan stopped at an oasis for water. "Why do I have to do my mission alone?"

"Come. Let's take a walk," said Malachi, motioning for her to follow. When they were far enough away to talk privately, he said, "The key that you're retrieving is called the Solitude Key. So, of course you must retrieve the key in solitude—alone. But not totally alone."

"What do you mean 'alone...but not totally alone?'"

"You will be alone—with God. That's what solitude is all about. Taking time to be with God. You're not often alone, are you, Emily?"

Emily couldn't deny it. Before the coronavirus struck, she rarely spent time by herself or alone with God. Can she help it if she loves being with people? Even during the lockdown, she spent as much time as possible on the phone with friends.

"Being with friends is great," said Malachi. "You're an extrovert, and extroverts get energized by being with people. But you don't leave any time to be with God."

"I'm easily bored when I'm not with friends."

"But Jesus is your friend too."

"I know, but..."

"Jesus said, 'I am the vine. You are the branches.'"

"And your point is...?"

"If we're branches, we must remain connected to the vine. If we don't, we cannot produce fruit. You must remain connected to Jesus if you want to produce the Fruit of the Spirit—love, joy, peace, forbearance, kindness, goodness, faithfulness, gentleness, and self-control."

"I'm not perfect, you know."

"None of us are. That's why we must make room for Jesus. He's the Living Water, the Bread of Life—all that you need to live."

"I suppose that's why you chose me to retrieve the Solitude Key," Emily muttered. "Trying to teach me a lesson."

"I know you can do this, with hope and faith. Faith is confidence in what we hope for and assurance about what we do not see."

She sighed. "And you won't even let Red help me...just a little bit?"

"This is your mission—yours alone. You must retrieve the key from the Garden of Weeden."

"A garden? In a desert?"

"We'll find the garden at the next oasis. But before we reach it, let me give you your secret weapons."

Isabella and Aiden hadn't been given weapons, so maybe Malachi was going to have mercy on her after all.

"A lightsaber?" she asked.

"Not quite. Here. Take. Through Christ, we are more than conquerors." Malachi handed Emily a small, red box—like a ring box—and a small glass bottle of clear liquid.

"Is this a special liquid with great powers?"

"It's just water."

*Water? Since when is water a secret weapon?*

"What about this ring case?" Emily asked. "Does it contain a ring of power, like in *The Lord of the Rings*?"

"Open it and see."

But when she clicked open the lid, she found inside what looked like a seed— perhaps the smallest seed she had ever laid eyes upon.

"This is my secret weapon?"

"It's a mustard seed. Use it wisely."

Emily stared at the little container of water and the tiny mustard seed and frowned. She didn't even like mustard. "I think I'd prefer the ring of power."

"Don't we all."

# THE GARDEN OF WEEDEN

It was late afternoon when they spotted the garden off in the distance. It was strange seeing this small slice of green, surrounded by a sea of brown sand. The garden was enclosed on all sides by a rock wall, about five feet high. And in the middle of the garden was a large, gnarly tree. A flag flapped from the tip-top branch.

"Cool. You get to climb a tree to reach the next flag," Red said to Emily. "Are you sure I can't help her, Malachi?"

Malachi put a hand on Red's shoulder—probably to keep him from running off again.

"I'm sorry, Red," Emily said, "but I must do this alone."

She loved climbing trees, so maybe this will be fun. It certainly beat walking across slowsand or trying to find a flag in the middle of a battle.

"The tree you see is called the Tree of Lifelessness," Malachi pointed out.

"Tree of Lifelessness? Don't you mean, the Tree of Life?" asked Emily.

"No. The Tree of Lifelessness. This tree, created by the Destroyers, will try to suck all of the faith and hope out of you. Without those, life is very hard."

Suddenly, this tree with its twisting branches seemed quite ominous. She slipped her hand into her right pocket to make sure the water and mustard seed were still there. Then she lifted her chin and marched off. Alone.

When she reached the garden wall, she looked up at the Tree of Lifelessness, which loomed above. She thought she could hear it snickering at her. Maybe it was just the wind. She climbed the rock wall and paused at the top and looked around the garden. The ground was covered with all kinds of weeds, which must be why they called it the Garden of Weeden. But what was there to fear? They were only weeds.

Slowly, carefully, she lowered herself to the ground and began to walk toward the huge tree, trying not to brush against any plants. Just in case they were poisonous.

So far so good.

Suddenly, she felt something latch onto her ankle, and she looked down in horror to see that a thorn bush had wrapped itself around her foot. The thorns jabbed through her socks, into her skin. But, worst of all, she suddenly felt an overwhelming hopelessness wash over her. She had never felt such despair. Emily crumpled to the ground.

Had the thorn plant injected her with something that made her feel hopeless?

Memories poured into her mind. She thought about all of the sad things in her life—things she had mostly forgotten. She thought about her first day of kindergarten, when she was so sad to see her mother go. She thought about when she was in a school play and forgot all of her lines. She thought about Maryann Palmer, the girl who was mean to her when she first came to her new school last year.

Emily felt like she didn't have the strength to move. She looked up at the tree and sensed it staring down on her, laughing. She began to feel that this entire mission was one big waste of time. What was the point of it all? It was like chasing after the wind.

Emily's mind filled with weariness. Her thoughts were like a heavy weight, dragging her down. Why were they even bothering with the keys? And how in the world were they ever going to defeat a Sand Dragon?

Another vine wrapped itself around her other ankle, and she could almost feel the hope being drained out of her. These plants sucked the life out of you, like sucking water out of the ground.

*Water!*

When you're in a desert, what do you hope for? You hope for water.

Emily suddenly remembered the water that she carried in her pocket—and the mustard seed. Mustering all of her strength, she reached into her pocket and drew them out.

When Emily opened the little red box, she felt a shudder run through all of the weeds in the garden. It's like they were afraid. Turning over the box, she watched as the mustard seed—this tiny speck—fell to the ground.

Nothing happened.

Then Emily unscrewed the lid on the glass container, tipped the bottle, and watched the small amount of water splash on the soil.

It was like dropping a bomb. All of the weeds drew back, releasing Emily's legs and coiling in on one another. The soil where the mustard seed landed began to move and churn, like there was something alive under the ground. Then, all of a sudden, a vine shot out of the soil, twisting and curling. And then flowers and leaves started popping all across the branches, like popcorn. The vine grew enormous, sending out shoots right and left. It was as if a year of growing had been jammed into one single moment.

But…most important, Emily felt hope rise back up in her, like an empty goblet being filled. A sweet smell filled her senses, and she looked around in amazement. The garden had transformed from weeds to flowers, loads of them. Red, yellow, blue, purple, orange, pink. The smell was powerful and pleasing. The weeds had shriveled to almost nothing.

Emily was bursting with new hope. She had one last job. Climb the tree and get the key.

## THE TREE OF LIFELESSNESS

The bottom branch of the tree was within easy reach. With a little jump, Emily wrapped her arms around the thick branch. But the moment she touched the tree's bark, she felt a tremendous jolt shoot through her body. She also felt all faith and hope leave her. This was a hundred times worse than how the weeds made her feel.

*I give up,* she thought. Immediately, she let go, landing with a thump on the ground. Emily sat up, rubbed her head, and waited for the feeling of hopelessness to fade. She was determined to see this through.

Taking a running start, she wrapped her arms around the bottom branch again and tried to haul herself up as fast as she could. But, once again, as soon as she touched the bark, it was like she could feel the faith and hope being pulled out of her. This time, she managed to stay on the branch, and she even climbed two branches higher—before she lost both her hope and her grip. She fell.

When Emily crashed to the ground, she thought for a moment that she had broken something. But she was all right. Brushing the dirt off of her clothes, she tried to think. What was it that Malachi said about faith? Faith was confidence in what we hope for and the assurance of what we cannot see.

*Confidence in what we hope for.* People were always telling her to be confident in herself—in her own talents. Every single movie said the same thing: Believe in your own strength. But the Bible told her to be confident in what we hope for. And what do we hope for? *God!*

It was a comforting thought.

Emily prided herself on being good in everything—sports, making friends, schoolwork. People expected her to be great. She felt a pressure to be perfect. But if she put her hope in God, she didn't have to be supergirl all the time. She could fall again and again, and God would pick her up.

Until this moment, Emily didn't fully understand that she wasn't alone in this mission. God was right beside her.

Powered by this thought, she hurled herself onto the branch once again. She felt the faith and hope begin to disappear, but she held on tightly to the branch and squeezed her eyes shut.

Then an amazing thing happened. When she closed her eyes, hope returned. Faith sparked.

She opened her eyes again, and hope began to fade. She closed her eyes. Faith and hope returned. Faith is being sure about what we cannot see, Malachi said. That's it!

Emily realized that she would have to climb the tree with her eyes closed. She stood up on the thick branch and felt around for the next branch higher. This was going to be impossible! But she remembered stories about a woman named Helen Keller, who went through life blind, deaf, and unable to speak. Helen couldn't see after she was eighteen months old, and yet she did amazing things. Surely, Emily could climb this tree with her eyes closed.

She reached the third branch, then the fourth. But when she reached for the fifth branch, she placed her right foot wrong and slipped. She fell, plunging downward. She scraped her arm on a branch going down but managed to grab another branch. For a brief moment, she opened her eyes and nearly lost all hope.

Squeezing her eyes shut again, she began to climb. Slowly. Carefully. Branch by branch by branch.

"Faith is the confidence in what we hope for and the assurance about what we don't see!" she shouted, clawing her way even higher. With her eyes closed, she didn't have any idea how close to the top she was, but she sensed she was near. If she fell now, she would surely break a bone. Or worse.

The higher she climbed, the thinner the branches became. The branches swayed back and forth, and she wondered if the tree was trying to throw her off. At last, she sensed that she had reached the top. A mighty wind roared across the desert, as the Destroyers tried one last attempt to flick her from the branch.

She also sensed that the flagpole was just within reach, so she extended her arm. She felt nothing but air. She was tempted to open her eyes, but she knew that if she did, she would lose all hope. The flagpole and the key were just barely out of reach. She wasn't sure how she knew it. She just did.

Emily would have to leap. She'd have to let ago of the branch and hurl herself at the flagpole! But that's impossible!

Impossible for Emily, that's for sure. But impossible for God?

She prayed like she never had before. She kept her eyes closed and listened.

The wind was blowing even harder now. The branch that she clutched swayed wildly in the wind, so she had to time this right.

Then, as clearly as someone whispering in her ear, she heard a voice say, "Jump."

So she did. With eyes squeezed shut, she threw herself forward, clawing at the air and wondering if she was about to crash to the ground. She was all alone in mid-air for one terrifying moment with nothing solid to hold onto.

And then…and then…

She felt the cool solidness of steel. A flag flapped against her face. She wrapped both arms tightly around the flagpole and held on for dear life. The wind roared in her ears, and the flagpole swayed wildly, back and forth. With eyes still closed, she ran her hand down the flagpole until she finally touched the key.

Don't drop it, don't drop it, she told herself. Riding that flagpole as it whipped in the wind was like riding an out-of-control amusement park ride.

She grabbed the key.

Then she fell.

But not far.

She managed to grab hold of a branch, even while clutching the Solitude Key in one hand. The wind had died down, the tree had stopped shaking, and her eyes were now wide open. Her hope was still alive. Her faith was stronger than ever.

Carefully, Emily pulled herself up onto a branch and took it all in. Straddling the branch, she stared across the land. The desert looked beautiful from so high up. It was like she could see forever.

"Thank you, Jesus!" she shouted for all to hear. Her voice carried for miles.

# TO BE CONTINUED ON PAGE 222.

#BEINGCHALLENGEKIDS

# DAY 27
## STOP FOR SOLITUDE
## SEEK GOD FIRST

### THE DAYS OF CREATION

Check out Genesis 1 in your Bible. Below, either draw or write in the six circles, describing what happened on the first six days of creation.

## IN THE BEGINNING...

DAY 1

DAY 2

DAY 3

DAY 4

DAY 5

DAY 6

Next, read Genesis 2:1-3. What happened in this passage? Draw a picture or write what happened on the seventh day.

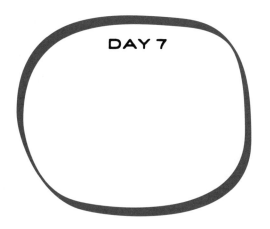

DAY 7

God spent six days making an incredible world and filling it with the sun, moon, and stars, then creatures of the air and sea, and finally the land animals and people.

But on Day 7, God chose to rest. He didn't have to rest. It wasn't like God was on low battery and needed to be recharged. He spent the day with Adam and Eve, enjoying His creation and seeing how everything worked.

God blessed the seventh day. He didn't do that for any other day. He made the seventh day holy, which means it's to be used for a special purpose.

# ADAM AND EVE'S CHECKLIST

If Adam and Eve were like a lot of us, their seventh day might've gone something like this.

*"All right God, I've got my checklist!" Adam said, bounding through the garden on the beautiful morning of the seventh day.*

*"What list?" God asked.*

*"My chore list. Yesterday, you put me in charge of creation. You said I should rule over the animals and every seed-bearing plant. Sooooo…I figured I'd give the orangutans a haircut and maybe polish some turtle shells and organize some birds into a choir and…"*

"Rest," God said.

"Rust?" Adam said. "You want me to clean some rust? Off of what?"

"Rest, Adam. I've made this day holy. It's a day to enjoy my creation."

Just then, Eve popped onto the scene, dragging a list about ten feet long. "Why aren't you giving the orangutan a haircut?" she asked Adam, as she picked a flower and tucked it behind her ear.

"God says we're to rest today," Adam said.

"Hmmmm, rest is not on my list," Eve said, looking over her sheet of paper.

"I want us to enjoy each other," said God. "I want to BE with you, spend some time with you. I want this day to be about you and me."

"But there's so much to do," Eve said.

"It will wait until tomorrow. Your strength comes from me, so you need to spend time with me."

Adam and Eve decided to trust God. They tore up their checklists and sat down on the ground to soak in God's creation. Adam sighed as he leaned back against a sheep and put his feet up on a tortoise. He toppled over when the sheep wandered off and the tortoise inched away.

"Remind me to find myself a good recliner," he said to Eve.

"Tomorrow," Eve said. "Worry about that tomorrow."

# FIRST THINGS FIRST

Sabbath means taking a day of the week to rest and enjoy everything connected to God. This day includes "solitude," which is being alone with God. Note the "with God" part. Solitude is not just about being alone. It's about being alone with God.

The very first time we see humans practicing Sabbath and solitude is on Day 7 of creation. Sabbath is so important that thousands of years later, God made it part of the Ten Commandments. The third commandment says, "Remember the Sabbath day and keep it holy."

There's that word "holy" again! God was not going to let this go.

# SOLITUDE COMES FIRST

Most people do not practice solitude. Like Adam and Eve in our story, we wake up ready to hit the road. We want action. What do I have to do? Where am I going to? Who am I going to see?

But Jesus often started His day with solitude. The Bible mentions that Jesus found time alone with His Father nearly 40 times in the Gospels. He often did it early in the morning, before anything else. Solitude comes first.

God loves us, and He knows what we need. He gave us the entire creation in which to live. The universe didn't just appear out of nowhere like some magic trick. God made it, and we were born into it. It's a gift.

So enjoy. Rest. Put your feet up on a recliner and enjoy God and His creation. You can always give your orangutan a haircut tomorrow.

# TARGET PRACTICE

We're going to take aim and see how much you practice solitude. Color in the ring on the target that connects to your answer. Remember, there isn't a right or wrong answer. Target practice is a way for you to see where you need to grow. Then you can set up some new targets to shoot for!

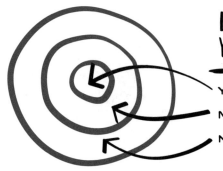

## DID YOU KNOW WHAT SOLITUDE WAS BEFORE YOU READ THIS CHAPTER TODAY?

YES

MAYBE, I'M NOT SURE.

NO

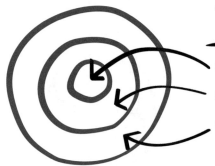

## DO YOU UNDERSTAND WHAT YOU MUST DO TO EXPERIENCE SOLITUDE?

I UNDERSTAND.

SOME, BUT I NEED TO LEARN MORE.

I TOTALLY DON'T GET IT.

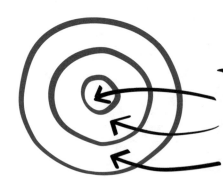

## IN THE FUTURE, HOW OFTEN DO YOU HOPE TO PRACTICE SOLITUDE?

ALWAYS (6-7 TIMES PER WEEK)

SOMETIMES, IF GOD WANTS ME TO. (1-5 TIMES PER WEEK)

NEVER, IT'S BORING! (0 TIMES PER WEEK)

# RED ALERT!

The Hebrew word for Sabbath is "Shabbat." It doesn't just mean "rest." It means: "STOP! Rest." It's the STOP sign of our week.

#BEINGCHALLENGEKIDS

# DAY 28

## IS BEING ALONE GOOD FOR YOU?

### THE QUIETEST PLACE ON EARTH

It's been called "the quietest room in the world," according to the *Guinness Book of World Records*. This room, in Orfield Laboratory in Minneapolis, is often used by companies to test their products to find out how loud they are. At -9 decibels, the room is so quiet that you can hear your heart beat and even the blood flowing through your body.

People can enter the room on tours, but after a couple of minutes, many feel uncomfortable and want to get out. Apparently, the longest anyone has ever stayed in that room was 45 minutes.

If you ever go in there, be on your best behavior. You wouldn't want to get a time out in a room like that!

Make your own pretend Orfield Lab. Play the Quiet Game with a friend or sibling. Use a timer to see who can be the quietest the longest.

YOUR TIME: _____    YOUR FRIEND'S TIME: _____

# TIME OUTS AND SOLITARY CONFINEMENT

Have you ever been in time out as a punishment? A time out means being kept out of a room or in a corner by yourself for a certain amount of time. It means being out of the fun.

Being alone is also a punishment for adults. If prisoners don't follow the rules in jail, they might end up in solitary confinement. They have to sit in a prison cell all alone for days. They don't even see people when they get their food. The food is slipped in through a little door. It's a terrible punishment.

Solitary confinement can make prisoners feel sad, anxious, and depressed. It can even make people feel sick. Many inmates say they have headaches, sweat, and feel dizziness; they lose weight and their stomach hurts when they're in solitary confinement.

Solitary confinement for more than 15 days can cause permanent damage.

What this means is that God created us to be around other people. We need friends and others. In Genesis 2:18, God said, **"It is not good for man to be alone. I will make a helper suitable for him."**

So, if quiet rooms and solitary confinement can drive us crazy, why are we talking about stopping for solitude? Isn't that like putting yourself in time out?

# TIME IN

Although God made us to be with others, we still need time to be alone. You spend more time alone than you think. You shower or bathe alone. You get dressed alone. And if you have your own room, you may sleep alone. When you're on your device or phone, much of the time you're alone.

Put a check mark next to the times you're alone. In the blank, write how much time you spend doing these things during a day.

☐ Brushing your teeth _____

☐ Getting dressed _____

☐ Taking a shower or bath _____

☐ Waking up before anyone else _____

☐ Going to bed at night _____

☐ Riding or walking home alone _____

☐ Playing alone _____

☐ Being alone at home without anyone else around _____

Solitude is not a time out. It's a TIME IN with God. Remember, solitude is about more than just being alone. It's about being alone with God. When we practice solitude, it isn't a punishment that we have to do. It's time together with God that we want to do. Even if it's difficult at first, the more we do it, the more we can learn to enjoy it.

King David in the Bible said he would rather spend time with God than do anything else. **"Better is one day in your courts than a thousand elsewhere,"** says Psalm 84:10.

# JESUS WAS ALONE

Jesus practiced solitude for many different reasons. Look up each Bible verse and match it with the reason for His solitude.

| | |
|---|---|
| **Luke 22:39-44** | After something really sad happens |
| **Luke 5:16** | To get ready for a big challenge |
| **Luke 6:12-13** | Before a big decision |
| **Mark 6:30-32** | When things get tough |
| **Luke 4:1-2, 14-15** | To pray |
| **Matthew 14:1-13** | To rest after a big job |

To get to know and love someone, you have to spend time with them. So, spend time alone with Jesus. He invites us to do that. **"Come near to God and he will come near to you,"** says James 4:8.

# CHALLENGE

On page 196, you marked some of the things you do alone. Your challenge is to take one of those times and make it a time to be with God. He's waiting! He's excited to spend time with you.

---

# DAY 29

## MAKE ROOM FOR GOD

### FILL 'ER UP!

Draw your favorite meal of all time on the plate below:

Imagine you're at your favorite restaurant and you just ordered your favorite meal.
But while you're waiting, the server brings you chips and salsa and a drink.

You're starving! You didn't have much for breakfast, and you can't wait for your food to arrive. The smell of delicious food floating through the restaurant is driving you crazy. So, after you gobble up all of the chips, your dad orders more. The chips are warm and crisp, just how you like them.

AT LAST your food arrives. It looks great, so you dig in. One bite. Two bites. Three bites. You're full.

Your mom and dad took you here because they knew it was your favorite place and this was your favorite meal. So you press on, even though your stomach is bursting. You take a fourth bite. Five.

Finally…You give up. You can't eat another bite. You didn't get to completely enjoy your favorite meal because you didn't leave room for it. Bummer.

## ANY ROOM FOR GOD?

Just like we sometimes don't leave room for good food, we sometimes don't leave room in our heart and mind for God. We fill up our days with so many things that there's no time left for God. These things are called "distractions."

Color in all of the distractions that might keep you from spending time with God.

Notice that these are not bad things. They're gifts from God for us to enjoy. But sometimes we fill up our days with so many good things that we forget about the very best thing of all—God.

# FOCUS ON THE FIVE

So what do you do when you're alone with God? How does it work? For answers, let's look at five key questions about solitude.

## WHO?

It's just you and Jesus. No one else.

## WHERE?

Go to a quiet place without any screens, people, or other distractions. One great place is your bedroom.

## WHEN?

You can be alone with God any time of the day or evening. Whatever works best. Maybe first thing in the morning or right after school. Maybe you're all alone at bedtime.

## WHY?

We do this to grow in our relationship with God.

## HOW?

When you spend time with God, think about a line from a song or a Bible verse. Say it out loud or repeat it in your head. Think about how wonderful God is or something amazing He has done.

# VOLUME DOWN!

You don't have to spend time with God in the quietest room in the world. (See Day 28.) But it helps if we turn off our loud, noisy, and distracting devices. So turn off the TV and your phone.

One of Jesus's most common phrases was: **"He who has ears, let him hear!" Matthew 13:9 (*English Standard Version*).** He didn't say "He who has earbuds, let him hear" or "He who has headphones on, let him hear." It's difficult to hear God's voice when your ears are filled with noise. So open your ears. God is speaking to you.

Also, the Bible talks about fixing our eyes on Him. Hebrews 12:1b-2a says: **"And let us run with perseverance the race marked out for us, fixing our eyes on Jesus, the pioneer and perfecter of faith."**

Keep both your ears and eyes open. Look for God in your day.

# CHALLENGE

Try some solitude right now. Find a comfortable place and try to think about the phrase, "fixing our eyes on Jesus." Have an adult set a timer for one minute or set a timer on your device. How did it go? Could you make it the entire sixty seconds? Could you go longer?

Don't get discouraged if your mind wanders. This is not an easy thing to do. The goal is to remove all distractions—music, books, and even napping. Just sit quietly with your eyes open—or closed, as long as you don't fall asleep. Listen for God. Imagine Him right in front of you, looking at you with love.

# DAY 30

## STOP FOR SOLITUDE

# WEAPONS OF MASS DISTRACTION

## WARNING! WARNING!

Take a look at these real-life warnings and try to guess what's being talked about. What is THEY?

THEY CAN NEGATIVELY AFFECT YOUR EYESIGHT.

THEY CAN CAUSE ANXIETY THROUGH TOO MUCH INFORMATION, STIMULATION, OR BRAIN OVERLOAD.

THEY CAN MAKE YOU LESS ACTIVE AND CAUSE HEADACHES.

THEY ARE ADDICTIVE AND CAN CAUSE YOU TO HAVE BAD SLEEP HABITS.

Are these warnings against smartphones? Computers? Television?

No. These are actual warnings about books, if you can believe it. These warning came from doctors, teachers, philosophers, and poets hundreds of years ago. The "experts" actually complained about the dangers of books!

Today, it would be really hard to find someone who's against reading. Today, we hear the opposite message from teachers, politicians, and doctors. They say reading is good for you, and it's true! Reading is a healthy, wonderful activity.

Of course, as with any good thing, not every book is good for us. Some books have even helped to trigger a war. As just one example, Adolf Hitler's book poisoned the minds of millions of people.

Like food, reading is good for you. But you still have to watch what you read—just like you have to watch what you eat.

# SCREEN OVERLOAD

If you thought those warnings were about electronic devices, you had good reason. People today say similar things about smartphones, iPads, and computers. That's because these devices are not always used in good ways.

Too much screen time can increase the risk of obesity, sleep problems, cyberbullying, and poor performance at school, says the American Academy of Pediatrics.

It's been estimated that kids, ages 8 to 12, spend about 4 hours and 36 minutes on screens every day. Most of that is watching TV, playing games, listening to music, and exploring social media. It's also been estimated that the average person checks his or her phone about 80 times a day; for young adults, the number is 150 times a day!

Sometimes, our devices can be weapons of mass distraction.

Try to think about how much time you spend, on average, on your screens in a typical day. If you need help figuring it out, ask a parent or guardian. Then multiply that number by 7 to find out how many hours you spend on screens in a week. Multiple it by 365 to find out how many hours you spend on screens in a year.

**HOURS PER DAY ON SCREENS:**

_____

**HOURS PER WEEK ON SCREENS:**

_____

**HOURS PER YEAR ON SCREENS:**

_____

# TO SCREEN OR NOT TO SCREEN

God isn't against new inventions and technology. He gave us the brains to invent them in the first place! But He doesn't want to see His children become slaves to these devices. He doesn't want our devices to become idols. (An idol is something we put in the place of God in our life.)

In Exodus 32, Moses went up Mount Sinai where he talked with God. Meanwhile, the Israelites got impatient and started grumbling. They were bored, so the Israelites decided to make an idol. They took all of the gold earrings from their wives, melted them down, and used them to create a golden calf. Then they made offerings to the idol and went wild.

Note that the Israelites took something positive and beautiful—gold earrings—and turned them into a golden calf. An idol. Once again, even good things can become a problem if we let them take control of our life.

The Israelites escaped slavery in Egypt only to become slaves to a golden idol. Likewise, don't become slaves to your screens. If we're spending hours and hours on our devices and only minutes or no time with God, something is wrong. Something is out of balance.

Of course, no matter how much time we spend in solitude, that doesn't make us perfect. We still need a Savior. We still need Jesus, who gave up everything to live and die for us. He defeated the devil because of His great love for us. You don't have to turn off that screen and spend time with Jesus to earn His love. You've had His love all along. God made us, loves us, and saves us. You won't find an app anywhere that can do that!

## CHALLENGE

Try to unplug today. Spend at least one hour putting all of your digital devices away. Go for as long as you can.

In addition to unplugging from your screens, spend some of that time in solitude.

# RED ALERT!

When Abram was alone, God came to him and said he was going to become the father of many nations. Abram's wife would finally have a child, and his descendants would become as numerous as the stars. God also changed Abram's name to Abraham. Great things happen when you're alone with God.
(Genesis 17)

# DAY 31

## STAY CONNECTED TO JESUS

### REMEMBER WHERE WE'VE BEEN

Remember...The habits of Jesus helped Him during His mission on Earth. You've been putting these habits into practice, week by week:

- **FRIENDSHIPS**
  We need other people to help us along the way.

- **SCRIPTURE**
  God's Word is the foundation on which we build our faith.

- **PRAYER**
  We're in relationship with God and can talk to Him any time.

- **SOLITUDE**
  Time alone with God makes you stronger spiritually.

Solitude helps us to remember that God is the source of our strength to accomplish our mission in life. But to receive this strength, we've got to remain connected to Him. When Jesus explained this idea to His disciples, He used the image of a garden, vine, and branches.

# BE FRUITFUL

The day before Jesus went to the cross to die, He had a meal with His disciples—the Last Supper. He knew He didn't have much time left on earth, so He answered their many questions. He also told them this:

> "I am the true vine, and my Father is the gardener. He cuts off every branch in me that bears no fruit, while every branch that does not bear fruit he prunes so that it will be even more fruitful. You are already clean because of the word I have spoken to you. Remain in me, as I also remain in you. No branch can bear fruit by itself; it must remain in the vine. Neither can you bear fruit unless you remain in me.

> "I am the vine; you are the branches. If you remain in me and I in you, you will bear much fruit; apart from me you can do nothing." **John 15:1-5**

Jesus told this story to His disciples so they'd remember that they need to stay connected to Him. Without our connection to Jesus, it's impossible for us to produce fruit. By "fruit," Jesus was talking about the Fruit of the Spirit.

**"But the fruit of the Spirit is love, joy, peace, forbearance, kindness, goodness, faithfulness, gentleness and self-control. Against such things there is no law,"** says Galatians 5:22-23. (By the way, "forbearance" means to endure suffering.)

If the branch of a vine gets cut off, it's useless. In the same way, without our connection to Jesus, we cannot produce Fruit of the Spirit in our life. When we're apart from God, the gardener of the world, we wither.

Below, write the name of Jesus somewhere next to the vine. Then color the vine and write your name on a branch. Finally, write or draw some of the Fruit of the Spirit next to the fruit on the vine.

# UNDERGROUND OPERATIONS

Before a plant can grow and produce fruit, many things need to happen that we can't see on the outside of a plant.

- It needs good soil.

- It needs water and sunshine.

- It needs to grow branches strong enough to hold the fruit. Sometimes it takes many years of growing before you ever see fruit.

In the same way, most of the things that we need to grow in our Christian life happen when no one is looking. For example...

- We need others. We all have different talents and abilities. When we work together, we can accomplish wonderful things (FRIENDSHIP).

- We need to be planted in the truth of God's Word, the Bible (SCRIPTURE).

- We need the Son (not the sun!) of God to talk with daily (PRAYER). Jesus said that if we drink of His water, we'll never be thirsty again.

- We need to be alone with God. When we stay connected to Jesus, we'll see the Fruit of the Spirit in our lives (SOLITUDE).

A branch doesn't make fruit just for itself. There is purpose for the fruit—to spread itself to others. When a fruit tree dies, the tree spreads seeds, which become new trees. God wants us to spread our fruit to others. He wants us to serve other people.

Being alone with God—solitude—gives us the time and space to grow, like a plant taking in rich nutrients. Before we know it, fruit begins to appear and we start spreading our seeds of love to others.

# CHALLENGE

During your solitude time with God today, enjoy some fruit. Find whatever is on your counter or in your pantry. Think about how being connected to God produces Fruit of the Spirit in your life. Think about all of the things that need to happen for fruit to be made. What type of Fruit of the Spirit is God creating in your life?

# DAY 32

## STOP FOR SOLITUDE

## WHISPERS OF GOD

---

### PARTLY CLOUDY WITH A CHANCE OF EARTHQUAKES

The prophet Elijah was on the run. King Ahab and Queen Jezebel were furious after the Lord made a fool out of their false god known as Baal. They wanted to kill Elijah, who fled to Horeb, the mountain of God, and hid in a cave.

There, God told Elijah to stand on the mountain because the Lord was about to pass by. 1 Kings 19:11b-13 (*The Message*) tells what happened next.

> **"A hurricane wind ripped through the mountains and shattered the rocks before God, but God wasn't to be found in the wind; after the wind an earthquake, but God wasn't in the earthquake; and after the earthquake fire, but God wasn't in the fire; and after the fire a gentle and quiet whisper.**

> **"When Elijah heard the quiet voice, he muffled his face with his great cloak, went to the mouth of the cave, and stood there. A quiet voice asked, 'So Elijah, now tell me, what are you doing here?'"**

God wasn't in the noisy events—the earthquake, wind, and fire. He was in a gentle whisper. When we get lost in the noise and busyness of life, Jesus comes and finds us. He whispers. He calls. God will speak to us, but we have to be quiet to listen. Solitude helps us find the quiet space to hear.

# FOUR TRUTHS

God says many different things to us, but here are four of the most important truths that He tells us in the Bible.

**1** I FORGIVE YOU.

**2** I LOVE YOU.

**3** I CHOOSE YOU.

**4** I'M COMING BACK FOR YOU.

Below are four stories about kids who heard the voice of God through the Bible. After each one, write down which of the Four Truths fits that story.

# GUILTY!

Devon stormed into his room and slammed the door as hard as he could. He had to get away from the disappointed looks of his parents.

The school had called to tell Devon's parents that he had been caught stealing. No one at school trusted him; the kids all hated him. And now his parents were heaping on the guilt.

He wasn't sure why he did it. He just wanted to be like everyone who had these awesome water bottles. So he swiped one. When the principal found it in his lunchbox, he pretended not to care that he had been caught.

But he did care. The sad look in his father's eyes bothered him the most. I just wish someone was on my side, he thought, flopping onto his bed. Then he remembered a verse from church:

**"If we confess our sins, he is faithful and just and will forgive us our sins and purify us from all unrighteousness." 1 John 1:9**

Devon sensed God whispering to him through this verse. It might take a long time to win back everyone's trust, but he realized he could survive this because God says _____ .

# RIPS IN LIFE

Ashlynn sank back in the seat of her dad's car. As she reached for her backpack, she noticed a tear in the car seat and heard the engine making a knocking sound. The last car they owned had died on the side of the road, so Ashlynn's uncle gave them this old car. But it wasn't going to last much longer.

No matter how hard her parents worked, they never seemed to have enough money for basic things, let alone a brand-new car. Ashlynn was given a school lunch because her family qualified for the free lunch program. Her clothes were either hand-me-downs or bought at the thrift store.

Ashlynn stared at the ceiling and thought, "God, why do so many people have so much, while we don't?"

Then she thought of the Bible verse from her devotional:

**"For I am sure that neither death nor life, nor angels nor rulers, nor things present nor things to come, nor powers, nor height nor depth, nor anything else in all creation, will be able to separate us from the love of God in Christ Jesus our Lord." Romans 8:38-39 (*English Standard Version*)**

The rip was still there and the engine continued to knock, but Ashlynn felt better—as if God had whispered in her ear. No matter how much or how little she had, God was reminding her that _____.

# THE INVISIBLE GIRL

Mariah sat alone behind the bleachers. It was a typical Friday night and everyone was watching her older sister Chantel compete. Mariah lived in Chantel's shadow.

Chantel was a soccer star and was pretty, outgoing, confident, smart, and funny. Mariah was just known as "Chantel's little sister." Even her parents seemed to spend all their time on the weekends at Chantel's events.

People weren't mean to Mariah. They just ignored her. She was invisible.

Some cool kids ran by, heading for the snack shack, but they never even saw her. She felt unimportant. Forgotten. "God, does anyone even see me?" she said to herself. "Who cares about me?"

As she looked across the field, she noticed an odd thing. One of the clouds almost seemed to be shaped like a cross. She sighed and thought about Sunday School and the verse they memorized:

**"You did not choose me, but I chose you and appointed you so that you should go and bear fruit—fruit that will last—and so that whatever you ask in my name the Father will give you." John 15:16**

She felt God whispering to her, reminding her of an important lesson:

_____ .

# WHO'S IN CONTROL?

Mark tossed and turned in his bed. His teacher, Mrs. Kempta, had told the class this morning that she would not be coming back to school. She had cancer and needed treatment.

Mrs. Kempta was Mark's favorite teacher, and fourth grade had been his best year so far. Now, everything would change. Why couldn't God just destroy all of the cancer in the world?

Mark got up for a drink of water and then fluffed his pillow. As he lay back down, he remembered a verse printed on some artwork in the dining room:

**"He who testifies to these things says, 'Yes, I am coming soon.' Amen. Come, Lord Jesus." Revelation 22:20**

Mark knew that God would get rid of all evil someday, even cancer. God had control over all things, including the things Mark didn't understand. His eyelids began to close and he yawned as he heard God whisper this truth:

_____ .

## CHALLENGE

Which of the Four Truths do you need to hear today?

_____

Who could you share one of those Four Truths with today?

_____

_____

_____

## RED ALERT!

When Elijah hid from King Ahab in the Kerith Ravine, he spent time alone with God. The Lord told him to go to Zarephath. There, a widow gave him food and water, and he also brought the widow's son back to life. God can give us directions when we're alone with Him. (1 Kings 17:2-24)

# DAY 33

## FILL YOUR MIND WITH GOD

---

### PARTY TIME!

Grab a friend and play the game "Would You Rather?" Which of these things would you rather do?

| | | |
|---:|:---:|:---|
| Ride a rollercoaster | OR | Ride in a canoe |
| Go to a music concert | OR | Go see a movie |
| Snow ski | OR | Water ski |
| Spend $50 at an arcade | OR | Spend $50 at Target |
| Go to a sports camp | OR | Go to a music camp |
| Play in snow on a mountain | OR | Play in sand on a beach |
| Have wings and fly | OR | Have gills and breathe underwater |
| Go to Disney World | OR | Have unlimited screen time with free Wi-Fi |

Wow! All of these options look like fun! If there's one thing people have in common, it's that everyone likes to have fun. In America, people spend tons of money and energy on entertainment. Vacations, toys, games, sports equipment, TVs, pools, and playgrounds all have the same purpose—fun. God gave us the world to enjoy, and there are so many ways to do that.

But in the midst of our fun, are we taking time be alone with God?

# BORING ISN'T ALL BAD

It's the worst to be bored. Or is it?

Did you know that your brain is more active when you're bored? In fact, you're the most creative when you're bored. When we seem to be doing nothing and our minds wander, our brains are actually busier than if we were concentrating on a task.

So, it can be tempting to think that being stuck at home on a Saturday afternoon is going to be terrible. But maybe alone time is just what we need—time to spend with God.

In the Bible, Paul writes in Colossians 3:2, **"Set your mind on things above, not on earthly things."** But what does it mean to think about "things above"? Paul is telling us that it's important to think about what's important to God.

The Bible tells exactly what those "important things" are:

> **"Finally, brothers and sisters, whatever is true, whatever is noble, whatever is right, whatever is pure, whatever is lovely, whatever is admirable—if anything is excellent or praiseworthy—think about such things." Philippians 4:8**

Practice what Philippians preaches. Write out what those words mean to you. Some of them might be about God, Jesus, or church. Some might not. That's OK! God made everything, and He loves hearing about what you enjoy.

# IN YOUR LIFE, WHAT IS...?

TRUE _____

NOBLE (GOOD) _____

RIGHT _____

PURE (NOT SINFUL) _____

LOVELY (BEAUTIFUL) _____

ADMIRABLE (LIKEABLE) _____

EXCELLENT _____

PRAISEWORTHY _____

# MAKE ROOM FOR THE KING

Solitude might not sound like fun, but God speaks to us when we're quiet. In solitude, we fill our mind with thoughts of God. We focus on Jesus. This is called Christian meditation.

Christian meditation shouldn't be confused with the meditation of other religions. With Christian meditation, we're not trying to empty our mind. We're filling ourselves with God.

Even people who don't believe in any religion talk about meditating. But once again, they're missing the most important thing: God. Without God, meditation and solitude might help us feel more relaxed for a little while. But they won't help us in the long run. They certainly won't give our life the purpose we desire.

God is unendingly imaginative. He's the most creative being who has ever existed and will ever exist. So, spending time with Him is anything but boring. He'll give ideas to you when you're stuck. He'll help you look at things in a new way.

If the king of some nation knocked on your door and asked to come in, you'd make room for him. You wouldn't say, "Sorry, it's just a little too crowded. Would you come back later?" You'd welcome him.

Do the same with the King of all Creation. Welcome Him.

# CHALLENGE

Meditation refers to focused thinking about something. Christian meditation is focused thinking on God.

In the Old Testament, Jewish people would write the name of God using four Hebrew letters: YOD HEY VAV HEY. These are translated into English as Y-H-W-H or Yahweh. You can say His name in two breaths:

**YOD**    *(breathe in)*

**HEY**    *(breathe out)*

**VAV**    *(breathe in)*

**HEY**    *(breathe out)*

Repeat this breathing pattern ten times quietly. Think about the fact that you can't take a single breath without God.

DAYS
**34-40**
OF THE 40 DAY
CHALLENGE

# KEYSTONE HABIT 5:

# CHOO CHUR

SE
CH

HAVE FUN COLORING THIS PAGE!
FIND MORE LIKE THIS AT BEINGCHALLENGE.COM/KIDS

# THE SANDS OF REDVALE

## PART 6

"You did it, little sis!" Isabella shouted, giving Emily a huge hug.

Over the years, Isabella was often jealous of Emily because her little sister had a knack for making friends at the drop of a hat. But in Redvale, Isabella's feelings had changed. In Redvale, she *rooted* for Emily. She was proud of her.

There must be something in the air.

"I didn't do it alone," Emily said, smiling widely. "I had help."

"You had help?" Red said. "Malachi, I thought you said Emily had to do her mission *alone*."

"She did do it alone—but not totally alone. She had God's help," said Malachi.

"Oh…I suppose that's okay then," muttered the fox.

Once again, the three Perez kids, plus Red, inserted the key into the Sand Box together. The Solitude Key slid in smoothly, then CLICKED when they turned it.

"Only one more key to go," Aiden said.

"But it will be the most difficult one to get," Melchior pointed out. "The final key, the Church Key, is hidden inside the Sand Sovereign's Sand Castle."

"Is it my turn now?" Red asked. "Do I get to find the Church Key?"

"This time, we work together as a team," Malachi said. "And that includes you, Red."

"All right!" Red shouted. Isabella had never seen the fox jump so high.

Emily pointed up at the flag still flapping from the top of the Tree of Lifelessness. "The flag has the picture of a silver cup on it. What's that mean?"

"It's the flag of John, the beloved disciple who was especially close to Jesus.

There's a legend that someone once tried to kill John by putting poison in his cup. But John survived and lived to old age on the island of Patmos, where he wrote the book of Revelation."

"A very confusing book," Aiden said.

"Revelation contains many mysteries," Malachi said. "But mysteries make life interesting, don't you think?"

"Mysteries drive me crazy," said Red. "For instance, I wanna know the mystery of what's inside this Sand Box we've been lugging everywhere."

"Patience. You'll learn in due time," Malachi said.

"How far to the Sand Castle?" Isabella asked.

"Three more flags away."

"Then what are we waiting for?" Aiden said. "All our food has turned to sand, and who knows how much of Cherryfield has turned to sand by now."

Malachi held up the Big Wilderness Guidebook. "All of the pages in our guidebook have also turned to sand. We're operating on faith now."

"And hope," said Emily. "Faith is confidence in what we hope for and assurance of what we can't see."

"Very good," Isabella said. "I didn't know you memorized Bible verses, Emily."

"I'm full of surprises."

"We all are," said Melchior as their caravan moved farther north with the setting sun to their left. Melchior continued to drag the Sand Box behind on the sled. He never seemed to tire.

# THE SAND CASTLE

Aiden had a hard time falling asleep that night because his stomach constantly growled. He had never gone a day without food, and his stomach was in open revolt. When he finally drifted asleep, it seemed that only moments passed before Red was shoving him on the shoulder.

"Wake up, Aiden! Shake a leg! Everyone's waiting for you!"

Groaning, Aiden dragged himself out of his tent, rubbing his eyes and stretching. Ten minutes later, they were back on the move. Today was going to be a hot one. The sun was already toasting the back of his neck.

The next flag they passed was the flag of Thomas. This flag showed the picture of an L-shaped measuring tool used by carpenters because it's believed that Thomas built a church in India. The picture also included arrows and a spear—weapons used to kill him.

Not long after, they came across the flag of James, displaying a staff, sword, and scallop shell. James was known for his pilgrimages—his treks across the land carrying his staff. That was the eleventh flag. One more to go.

They were still a good distance away when they first caught sight of the Sand Castle. From faraway, it looked like one of those beautiful sandcastles that people build on Florida beaches. But the closer they got, the more obvious it was that this castle was huge! It was bigger than the Medieval Times castle they sometimes went to for fun.

When they were close, they got down on their bellies and studied the lay of the land. Borrowing Emily's binoculars, Aiden spotted soldiers on the ramparts and marching in front of the castle. These soldiers carried trombones, tubas, and trumpets.

"I suppose those trumpets blast sand, just like the others we saw," he said to Malachi.

"That's right. Sandblasters."

Just then, a large shadow fell across them. When Aiden looked up, his heart nearly stopped. A huge dragon soared directly overhead, breathing out great blasts of sand. The monster was light brown—the color of sand. The Sand Dragon ignored them, flapping toward the castle.

"I never thought I'd ever see a sand-breathing dragon," Emily said.

"Or any kind of dragon," Isabella added. "I'd hate to meet that thing face-to-face."

"We may have to before this is up," said Malachi. "When the Sand Dragon breathes out sand, it also releases those invisible sandspinners."

"You mean the dragon is releasing the things turning everything to sand?" asked Aiden.

"That's right," said Melchior. "To stop the sandspinners, we must stop the dragon." Malachi leaped to his feet and began to stride toward the Sand Castle. "But first we need to get inside that castle. Let's go!"

"We're just going to knock on the front door?" said Aiden, hurrying to catch up.

"Sometimes the best plans are the simplest ones," said Malachi. "The Sand Sovereign loves traveling musicians. So we're going to say you're here to sing, and I'll use the trumpet. You've still got that trumpet, don't you, Aiden?"

"Well…yes," he said. "It's packed away in the supplies."

"Good. The guards will think it's a sandblaster, not a trumpet, so keep it out of sight for now."

"You want us to sing?" Isabella said. "Uh…but we're not the best of singers."

"You'll do fine together," Malachi assured them.

"What happens if the Sand Sovereign hates our music?" Aiden asked.

"He'll probably throw us all in prison," Malachi said matter-of-factly.

"You really think he'd throw us in prison just for not liking our singing?"

"Maybe not. He might toss us to the Sand Dragon instead."

Aiden wished he hadn't asked.

# AMAZING GRACE

At the front gate of the Sand Castle, they were met by two guards. Malachi calmly explained that the three children were singers who had traveled a long way just to perform for the Sand Sovereign.

"They sing?" said one of the guards, eying the three kids.

"Show him," Malachi said to the children.

"Really?" Emily whispered back. This was going to be bad, really bad. Isabella was right when she said they weren't very good singers.

"Don't be shy," urged Malachi. "Just sing 'hello.' You might be surprised."

"I guess so," said Emily, shrugging. She prepared for the worst.

"Helloooooooo," she sang, hitting a high note. As expected, it didn't sound all that good. But then Isabella and Aiden added their voices.

"Helloooooooo," sang Isabella, hitting a middle note.

"Helloooooooo," sang Aiden, hitting a low note.

Amazing! When they all sang together, their voices sounded pretty good. How can that be?

The guard stared at them, scratching his chin. "Actually, not bad. You may enter." The guard stepped aside and waved them by.

"Thank you, kind sir," said Melchior as they strolled through the outer gatehouse and entered within the walls of the castle. Melchior continued to pull the sled carrying the Sand Box, and no one stopped him.

Directly ahead was the inner gatehouse and more guards. But when Emily, Aiden, and Isabella did a bit of harmonizing, the guards broke into smiles and let them enter the central courtyard.

"I don't get it," said Emily. "We sound pretty good together. Even Isabella is singing on tune, and she's normally awful."

"That's harsh!" exclaimed Isabella. "You're not very good either."

Aiden giggled. "She's right, Em."

"And who are you to laugh?" Emily fumed, turning on Aiden. "At church, you try to sing louder than everyone else, as if it's a contest. But singing loud doesn't make you a better singer, especially when you're singing off tune."

"Guys, this is no time be arguing," said Melchior.

"When should they be arguing?" asked Red.

"Ideally, they shouldn't be arguing at all," pointed out Malachi. "But especially not now. We're in the inner ward of the castle."

Emily, Isabella, and Aiden stopped their bickering and gazed around. Emily was amazed by the strangeness of the place. It looked exactly like a real castle, except for one very important difference. The walls were made completely out of packed sand, not stone.

"So where's the final flag and key that we're after?" Aiden asked. "Is the flag flying from one of the towers?"

"I'm afraid it's not that easy," said Malachi. "The flag and the key are in the dungeon. And if I'm not mistaken, the dungeon is at the bottom of that tower." Malachi pointed to a tower rising up just to their left. "What we need now is a distraction. If you three are done with your arguing, it's time for you to begin singing."

"Here? Now?" Emily said. "But we don't have any songs memorized."

"No problemo," said Red, reaching into a saddlebag and pulling out a hymnal. "A lot of the pages have turned to sand, but there are some hymns you can still read."

"I suggest you start with 'Amazing Grace,'" said Malachi, taking the hymnal from Red and opening it to that song.

"You really think we can do this?" said Isabella. "I'm much better on the violin than singing."

"And I'm better on the piano," said Emily.

Malachi handed the open hymnal to Aiden. "As long as you sing together, you'll be fine. While you sing, Red will retrieve the key."

"I will?" said Red. "Fantastic!"

For their performance, Malachi had the three of them stand at the top of a flight of stairs. Emily was terrified because she didn't think it was wise to draw attention to themselves. A small crowd began to gather. Most of them were soldiers, carrying sandblasters. If the soldiers didn't like their music, would they start firing sand at them?

Isabella was the first to begin, but she started too soon! What was she doing? She should've waited for them to start together. Singing alone, her voice sounded like a water buffalo in pain.

*"Amazing Grace! How sweet the sound*
 *That saved a wretch like me!"*

The sound wasn't at all sweet. Her singing was wretched, and people began to snicker. If there were tomatoes handy, listeners would probably be getting ready to throw them. Quickly, Emily and Aiden joined in, filling in with the harmonies.

 *"I once was lost, but now am found;*
 *Was blind but now I see."*

Suddenly, their voices blended smoothly, and Isabella's croaking transformed to something beautiful. Amazing! The crowd began to grow.

*"Twas Grace that taught my heart to fear,*
 *And Grace, my fears relieved;*
 *How precious did that Grace appear*
 *The hour I first believed."*

This is nice, Emily thought, as she became increasingly comfortable. She and Aiden exchanged smiles and so did Isabella. Then, out of the corner of her eye, Emily spotted Red scamper off toward the tower, with Malachi at his side. Malachi had grabbed Aiden's trumpet and carried it along—but she had no idea why. She assumed they were off to retrieve the fifth and final key.

*Please go smoothly*, she prayed, but she had a hunch it wouldn't. Nothing was ever easy around here.

## THE DUNGEON

Red slipped inside the tower at ground level and saw an immediate problem. A guard holding a trumpet stood beside a trapdoor, which probably led down into the dungeon.

"Halt! No farther," said the guard, raising his trumpet like a sandblaster and taking aim.

"Sorry. Wrong room," Red said, starting to turn around to flee. But Malachi stood his ground. He carried Aiden's trumpet and held it up for the guard to see.

"Have you ever played your trumpet?" Malachi asked. When the guard responded with a puzzled look, Malachi put the trumpet to his mouth.

Alarmed, the guard shouted, "What do you think you're doing? Put down your sandblaster!"

"It's not a sandblaster," said Malachi. And before the guard could stop him, the beautiful music of "Amazing Grace" rose from Malachi's trumpet and filled the room. The guard's eyes went wide.

"Amazing! How did you do that?"

"Simple. I can show you if you'd like." While Malachi explained how a trumpet really worked, he gave a nod in Red's direction. Slowly, carefully, the fox slipped next to the trapdoor and quietly eased it open. The way down into the dungeon was on a rope, which dangled into the darkness.

Red grabbed hold of the rope and shimmied down into the gloom. The light streaming down into the dark hole revealed a truly terrifying sight. The huge dragon, made entirely out of sand, was curled up in the dungeon, fast asleep.

Red was no longer excited that he had been chosen for this mission. Why didn't Malachi pick one of the others?

# THE SAND SOVEREIGN

Isabella, Emily, and Aiden continued to sing, with growing confidence and pleasure. But as they sang, the page of their hymnal suddenly and shockingly began to turn to sand. They were losing words as the page slowly transformed to sand, so they sped up the song.

*"Through many dangers, toils, and snares,*
*I have already come;*
*'Tis Grace that brought me safe thus far,*
*And Grace will lead me home."*

"What's the meaning of this? Will someone tell me what's going on?" boomed a voice from Isabella's right. Glancing sideways, she saw a king of sorts stride into the open courtyard. People fell to their knees and bowed their heads to the ground as he passed. This had to be the Sand Sovereign. A little dog ran jauntily at the king's side.

Should we bow? Isabella wondered. She hated the idea of bowing to a villain like him. So she kept on singing, and so did Emily and Aiden. Her voice almost cracked in fear because only one verse on the page hadn't yet turned to sand.

*"When we've been there ten thousand years,*
*Bright shining as the sun,*
*We've no less days to sing God's praise*
*Than when we'd first begun."*

"Stop! Stop! Stop!" the Sand Sovereign shouted, waving his hands in their faces. Even the king's little dog spoke up in a squeaky voice: "Stop, stop this instant by royal decree!"

By this time, the page of their hymnal had completely turned to sand. So they had no choice but cease their singing.

"Who told you that you could sing in my castle?" the king demanded.

"Yeah, who told you?" echoed the little dog, a poodle from the looks of it. Isabella was too terrified to answer. Fortunately, Melchior was still there to speak up for them.

"These children have traveled a long way, sire, because they heard that you love beautiful music," said the camel.

The Sand Sovereign stared at each of the kids, as if trying to burn a hole in them with his eyes. He was a stocky man with thick, black eyebrows, a double chin, and bushy beard speckled with sand. His crown appeared to be made completely out of sand; his long, kingly robe was also covered with a fine coating of sand.

"I do like a good song," said the Sand Sovereign. "But it has to be a quiet song. You know I can't have anyone singing too loudly within my castle grounds."

"Why is that, sire?" Melchior asked.

*"You know."*

"I don't, sire."

"The walls. Too much sound can...can be trouble."

Isabella stared at the sand-packed walls, and it dawned on her what he meant. The walls were not strong. If people sang too loudly, the walls might just crumble.

"Sing outside the walls all you like," said the Sand Sovereign. "But no more singing inside the castle grounds! That is my command!"

"That is our command!" barked the royal dog.

Isabella, Emily, and Aiden exchanged glances. What do they do now?

"Can you find a really loud song in that hymnal?" Isabella whispered to Aiden.

# THE CHURCH KEY

Red continued to clutch the rope, dangling only two feet above the snoring snout of the Sand Dragon. The monster was curled up, only a couple of feet away from a flagpole rising from the floor. Could it be…?

The fifth and final key dangled from the flagpole. The Church Key.

Red dropped to the ground and tiptoed toward the Sand Dragon. The monster's mouth was partway open as he slept, and he breathed out puffs of sand. With each exhale, a blast of sand hid the flagpole for just a second. Red would have to grab the key between the dragon's breaths.

*WHOOSH!* The dragon exhaled, sending out a cloud of sand. When the cloud cleared away, Red made his move. He dashed for the flagpole and grabbed the Church Key, just as the dragon breathed out another puff of sand. The sand blasted the little fox in the face, and he began coughing.

He also dropped the Church Key.

Red watched in horror as the key fell on the front paw of the Sand Dragon and made a jangling sound. Red held his breath and waited to see if the dragon would awake. But the monster still seemed to be asleep, breathing out another puff of sand. The key was lying there, easily within reach. Carefully, quietly, Red reached out, and his paw curled around the keys. Gently, gently…he lifted the Church Key.

But when he looked up, he found the Sand Dragon staring at him with two huge, wide-open, bloodshot eyes. Red turned and ran for his life.

## TO BE CONTINUED ON PAGE 268.

# DAY 34

## CHOOSE CHURCH

## SMALL STEPS AND GIANT LEAPS

### SMALL, SMART CHOICES

Have you ever seen a builder constructing a house in your neighborhood? Sometimes, it's not easy to see what has changed each day. The changes at the construction site are often small and slow. But over time, the house takes shape, and pretty soon you're looking at a beautiful home, ready for someone to move in.

Choosing Church is a lot like that. Faithfully going to church every week may not seem like a big deal. But the Holy Spirit is building something in you, week after week. You're growing and changing.

When Neil Armstrong became the first person to step on the Moon, he famously said, "That's one small step for a man, one giant leap for mankind." When you choose to go to church regularly, you're taking many small steps in your walk with Jesus. But these small, smart choices add up to one giant leap in your faith.

### CONSISTENCY MATTERS

When you faithfully and regularly do something, that's called being "consistent." Before airplanes take off, pilots always go through a checklist of things to do.

They're consistent, and it saves lives. When a football kicker is getting ready to kick a game-winning field goal, they're on the sidelines practicing, practicing, practicing. They're consistent, and it wins games.

In the church, being consistent also matters. Here is what the Bible said people did regularly (consistently) in the early church:

> **"They devoted themselves to the apostles' teaching and to fellowship, to the breaking of bread and to prayer. Everyone was filled with awe at the many wonders and signs performed by the apostles. All the believers were together and had everything in common. They sold property and possessions to give to anyone who had need. Every day they continued to meet together in the temple courts. They broke bread in their homes and ate together with glad and sincere hearts, praising God and enjoying the favor of all the people. And the Lord added to their number daily those who were being saved." Acts 2:42-47**

In this passage from Acts, circle the different things that people in the church were doing every day.

We may not be able to Choose Church every day, but we can choose it once a week. It's estimated that a person is typically awake for 112 hours per week and asleep for 56 hours. Surely, we can give one hour out of those 112 to go to church.

Jesus doesn't tell us an exact number of times we should attend church every month. But he tells us we should gather together regularly as a people.

# I CHOSE YOU

Choose Church because God chose you.

Remember, however, that you'll not always be perfect in Choosing Church. Sometimes, we'll choose other things that seem more exciting to us. What's most important is that we know that Jesus always chooses us.

- He chose you when He became a baby and came to earth.

- He chose you when He was twelve and stayed behind to listen to teachers at the Temple.

- He chose you when He healed the sick and preached Good News.

- He chose you when He went to the cross and died for our sins.

- He chose you when He rose again and defeated death.

- He chose you at your baptism, when you became part of God's family.

# TARGET PRACTICE

Let's find how involved you are at church. Color the ring of each target that most accurately answers the question connected to it. This will help you set some targets to shoot for.

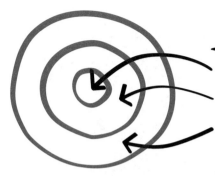

## HOW OFTEN DO YOU GO TO CHURCH OR SUNDAY SCHOOL?

EVERY SUNDAY (4 TIMES PER MONTH)

SOMETIMES (2 TO 3 TIMES PER MONTH)

ALMOST NEVER (0 TO 1 TIME PER MONTH)

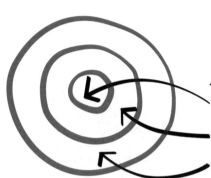

## IS YOUR FAMILY IN A SMALL GROUP OR PART OF ANOTHER CHURCH ACTIVITY OUTSIDE OF SUNDAY MORNING?

YES

MAYBE, I'M NOT SURE

NO, NOT YET

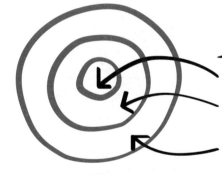

## DO YOU HAVE FRIENDS AT CHURCH?

ALWAYS!

I KNOW SOME PEOPLE THERE. WE'RE SORT OF FRIENDS.

NO, I DON'T KNOW ANYONE AT CHURCH.

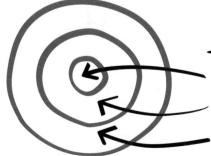

## DO YOU HELP AT CHURCH?

ALWAYS

SOMETIMES

NEVER

# DAY 35

## CHOOSE CHURCH

# MAGNIFY JESUS

---

### MARY MAGNIFIES THE LORD

Before Jesus was born, His mother, Mary, went to visit Elizabeth. Both women were expecting babies. But when Mary approached, the baby within Elizabeth leaped. (That baby would grow up to be John the Baptist.)

Then Mary exclaimed, **"My soul magnifies the Lord, and my spirit has rejoiced in God my Savior!" Luke 1:46-47 (*NKJV*).**

But what did she mean when she said, "My soul magnifies the Lord"? What did she mean by "magnify"?

Sometimes, "magnify" means making small things look bigger, like with a magnifying glass. But other things, like a telescope, make big things look closer to their real size. From earth, the Moon looks pretty small. But a powerful telescope makes the Moon look closer to its real size—which is huge.

God is bigger than we can imagine. So, when we magnify the Lord, that means we're trying to tell people just how big He really is. We do that through our praise. When Mary said her soul magnified the Lord, she was trying to tell Elizabeth just how BIG God was. She was praising Him.

# CHOICES

When we praise God every week at church, we too are magnifying Him. That's why it's so important to choose to meet together as a church.

"But wait!" you might say. "I don't get to Choose Church for myself. My grandma just tells me I have to go to church! Sometimes I wish I could sleep in."

Someone else might say, "I wish I could go to church more often, but my dad won't go, and my mom works at the hospital on Sundays and can't take me. I can't choose to go by myself. So I only go when my aunt takes me."

If other people are the ones who choose whether you go to church or not, you're not alone. Did you know that Jesus had someone else Choose Church for Him the first time He went? Jesus was only eight days old when he first started going to church.

Luke 2:22-40 tells how Joseph and Mary brought baby Jesus to the Temple in Jerusalem. There, they sacrificed a pair of doves and two young pigeons, because they were too poor to afford a lamb. This sacrifice was a sign that Jesus had joined a church family.

When they returned home, Jesus went regularly to synagogue—the Jewish church. Even though He was too young to decide to go on His own, God put people in His life to help Him Choose Church. Their decision made a huge difference in His life.

You too have people in your life to help you Choose Church. On mornings when it might feel nice to stay in your cozy bed, there are people who will get you moving. They know there is so much that God wants to show you. They know this truth: For God to show you His wonders, you must show up.

# PETER, THE ROCK STAR

If you go to Caesarea Philippi in Israel, you can find a cave there, which pagans believed was the entrance to Hades—the world of the dead. Somewhere in this area, Jesus asked His disciples, **"Who do you say I am?"**

Peter spoke up boldly. **"You are the Messiah, the Son of the Living God."**

JESUS IS THE MESSIAH,
THE SON OF THE LIVING GOD.

Then Jesus replied, **"Blessed are you, Simon son of Jonah, for this was not revealed to you by flesh and blood, but by my Father in heaven. And I tell you that you are Peter, and on this rock I will build my church, and the gates of Hades will not overcome it." Matthew 16:15-18**

Jesus said He would build His church on the rock of Peter's answer—**"You are the Messiah, the Son of the Living God."** (By the way, the name "Peter" means "rock.")

The Truth of Jesus the Messiah is the foundation holding up our Church. This Truth also holds our lives together.

# CHALLENGE

Track your weekly church attendance below. Color in each footprint to show how many times you have attended church in the last six weeks.

Even on weeks when you can't attend, think about how you can still Choose Church. If you get sick or the weather is bad, find a way to Choose Church at home. Listen to a Bible app, watch the performance of a popular worship song or hymn on YouTube, Pause to Pray, or Seek Solitude.

# RED ALERT!

The Church produced some of the most famous scientists in history. Nicolaus Copernicus, a Christian, changed the world with his idea that the planets orbited the sun. Gregor Mendel founded the science of genetics and Charles Babbage is the father of the computer. The list goes on and on.

# DAY 36

## CHOOSE CHURCH

# THE CHURCH ISN'T PERFECT, BUT GOD STILL LOVES IT

### DEN OF ROBBERS

Jesus got angry sometimes. One of the best examples of this was when He overturned tables in the Temple. He was angry because certain people forgot what the Temple was all about. They became more interested in money, and they made a real mess of things. These were the "money changers."

The Book of Mark describes the dramatic scene with the money changers this way:

"On reaching Jerusalem, Jesus entered the temple courts and began driving out those who were buying and selling there. He overturned the tables of the money changers and the benches of those selling doves, and would not allow anyone to carry merchandise through the temple courts. And as he taught them, he said 'Is it not written: "My house will be called a house of prayer for all nations"? But you have made it a "den of robbers."'

"The chief priests and the teachers of the law heard this and began looking for a way to kill him, for they feared him, because the whole crowd was amazed at his teaching." Mark 11:15-18

What was going on here? Why did Jesus start turning over tables? Who were the money changers?

In the Temple, people bought lambs, doves, and pigeons to sacrifice. But people came from all over carrying many different types of coins. They had to have them changed (or traded) for Tyrian shekels. Some believe, however, that the money changers were cheating people. They were also turning the Temple into a place for buying and selling. They were more concerned about money than people.

After Jesus drove out those who were buying and selling, Jesus said, **"My house will be called a house of prayer for all nations."**

No church is perfect. But as a house of prayer, the church should be a safe place for all kinds of different people to come together.

# THIS HAD BETTER BE FUN

Sometimes, we Choose Church for the wrong reasons. We might find ourselves rating a church like we would a business.

- Is this church fun?

- Do I like the snacks?

- Are people friendly?

- Is the music too noisy or not my style?

- Do the teachers or pastor talk about things that interest me?

It's OK to think about these things. But they aren't the heart of a church. The heart is Jesus. We go to church to learn more about God and who He is. We go to church to serve others. We go to church to be around other believers and support others through tough times.

Sometimes, it is not all about you. Always, it is about Jesus.

# CHURCH SQUABBLES

People are people, so arguments are bound to happen in a church. The Bible describes steps to take if you have a disagreement with someone.

> "If a fellow believer hurts you, go and tell him—work it out between the two of you. If he listens, you've made a friend. If he won't listen, take one or two others along so that the presence of witnesses will keep things honest, and try again. If he still won't listen, tell the church. If he won't listen to the church, you'll have to start over from scratch, confront him with the need for repentance, and offer again God's forgiving love."
> **Matthew 18:15-17 (*The Message*)**

What are the four steps that Jesus tells us to take when we have a problem with someone in the church?

**1** _____

**2** _____

**3** _____

**4** _____

We need the Church because we need relationships. But even more important, we need the Church because we need Jesus.

## CHALLENGE

The very first thing that people look at when they visit a church is friendliness. You can make a difference by saying hello to a new person in church. How else can you help to make your church a friendly place for old friends and new visitors? What do you love about your church?

_____

_____

_____

_____

## RED ALERT!

Some of the most powerful events started in the Church. The civil rights movement, fighting for equal rights for African Americans, came out of the Church. The movement that brought down the Wall dividing Berlin, Germany, started in the Church. Thier slogan was "swords into plowshares," based on a Bible verse.

# DAY 37

## CHOOSE CHURCH

# BEATING THE ODDS

---

### A WORLD OF TROUBLE

It can be dangerous to be a Christian, depending on where you live. There are many countries where people cannot worship God like we do. In some places, it's illegal to gather for prayer or even own a Bible. Here are 9 countries where you would either be treated differently, fined, imprisoned, or punished even worse if you are a Christian:

1. NORTH KOREA
2. AFGHANISTAN
3. SOMALIA
4. LIBYA
5. PAKISTAN
6. SUDAN
7. YEMEN
8. IRAN
9. CHINA

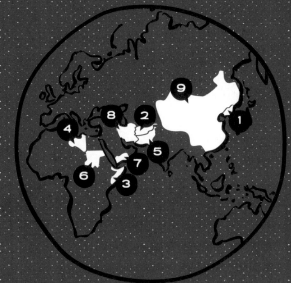

Even when terrible and unfair things happen to the Church, we trust God's plan. But trusting God's plan doesn't mean we sit around, relax, and let Him do all of the work. We are part of God's plan.

# AN UNFAIR FIGHT

One time, when Saul was King of Israel, the Philistine enemy had WAY more soldiers than the Israelites. As a result, many Israelites went into hiding or fled back over the Jordan River.

But it gets worse. The Israelites had only two weapons. Not two weapons per person. *Two for the entire army.* That's because the Philistines had taken away all of the weapons, except the ones owned by King Saul and his son Jonathan.

Jonathan had had enough. He told his armor bearer, **"There's no rule that says God can only deliver using a big army. No one can stop God from saving when he sets his mind to it." 1 Samuel 14:6 (*The Message*)**

Jonathan knew that even when the odds are stacked against us in the world, God is on our side. And if God was on his side, he didn't have to worry about who he was up against: one, two, or even a massive army.

Then something totally crazy happened. Jonathan and his armor bearer stormed into the Philistine camp like they were on the Marvel Avengers team. When they killed about twenty people, panic filled the Philistine army. Then an earthquake started shaking the ground.

King Saul and 600 soldiers were hiding and watching all this happen. When they rushed to the battle to help fight, they found that the Philistines were swinging their swords wildly, killing each other! It was crazy! The Philistines were killing their own side.

As word spread of what was happening, Israelites who had fled came back. According to the Bible, **"God saved Israel! What a day! The fighting moved on to Beth Aven. The whole army was behind Saul now—ten thousand strong!—with the fighting scattering into all the towns throughout the hills of Ephraim."** 1 Samuel 14:23 (*The Message*)

## KEEPING SCORE

God used the faith of just two people to inspire an entire army. Did you notice how the number of Israelites kept increasing as more and more of them saw what God was doing? Fill in the missing numbers below.

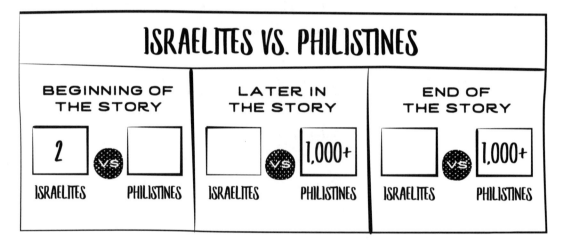

Just like the Israelites, we don't have the weapons to fight on our own power. We need God, and He will give us what we need. We only have to trust in Him.

## JOIN GOD'S TEAM

God invites you to be a part of His plan and part of His team, even if you feel you're not good enough. Jesus went up as one person, alone, on the cross.

He carried the sins of the world on His shoulders, and He fought against our most powerful enemy—Satan. But He came out a conqueror.

When you join the Church, you join the team. When you Choose Church, you're part of a long history. You join a long line of people who chose Jesus over everything—and conquered death.

## CHALLENGE

Read the entire story in 1 Samuel 13-14 on your own or as a family. What is God inviting you to be a part of? Pray for Christians who live in countries hostile to Christianity. Be thankful for the freedom you have to Choose Church. Not everyone can.

Finally, this is a hard one, but pray for our enemies. They do not understand what they are doing. Pray that God can open their eyes. Pray they can know that Jesus loves them and wants to be their Savior.

## RED ALERT!

The Christian Church led the movement against slavery in both England and the United States. In England, a Christian named William Wilberforce led the movement to abolish slavery. In America, many who helped slaves escape were Christians, including Harriet Tubman.

# DAY 38

## CHOOSE CHURCH

## DISCOVER YOUR GIFT

---

### THE RIDDLER

Here's a riddle for you…What do the five things below have in common?

- A MASSAGE

- A MINT

- GLASSES

- SCENTED CANDLES

- A HEARING AID

Write your answer here:

### THAT MAKES SENSE

Did you guess that all of those things have to do with our five senses—touch, taste, sight, smell, and hearing? If so, give yourself a reward.

Just as a body has different senses and different parts, the Church is a Body with many different parts. Check out 1 Corinthians 12:12 to read where the Bible compares the Church to a body, with people bringing many different gifts. In the Church, some people are hands, some are ears, and some are eyes.

Everyone has a gift, but no one has every gift. An ear doesn't try to see, an eye doesn't try to hear, and a hand doesn't try to kick a soccer ball. Remember, Church isn't just about showing up on Sunday. It's about using your gift to help the Church.

So…what is your gift?

Today is all about the Challenge. To discover what your spiritual gift might be, dive into the questions below.

# CHALLENGE

Have an adult or older sibling help you fill out the Spiritual Gifts test below. Answer each question with a number from 1 to 5. Here is what each number means:

NEVER—1  SELDOM—2  SOMETIMES—3  OFTEN—4  ALWAYS—5

**1.** I see things as being either right or wrong, good or evil. _____

**2.** I love to work with my hands, and I'm good at it. _____

**3.** I find great joy in learning. _____

**4.** I love to talk almost all the time. _____

**5.** Giving to others makes me joyful. _____

**6.** I get great joy from accomplishing something. _____

**7.** I get sad and angry when bad things happen to people. _____

**8.** I speak my mind; I'm outspoken. _____

**9.** I find great joy in helping others. _____

**10.** I love teaching people about things. _____

**11.** I am very happy and have a balanced personality. _____

**12.** I do everything with all my heart. _____

**13.** I thrive on competition; I always want to be first or the best. _____

**14.** I look for the good in people and ignore the bad. _____

**15.** I tend to be a little negative. _____

**16.** I am usually shy and easily embarrassed. _____

**17.** It's easy for me to speak and express my thoughts clearly. _____

**18.** I like to tell people "good job." _____

**19.** I am very imaginative. _____

**20.** It's very important that my friends are loyal to me. _____

**21.** I find great joy in showing love to someone who is hurting. _____

**22.** I feel that I am right most of the time. _____

**23.** I like helping others before I help myself. _____

**24.** I have strong beliefs and opinions. _____

**25.** I have a very positive outlook on life. _____

**26.** I do not have a lot of friends, just a few best friends. _____

**27.** I enjoy leading and telling others what to do. _____

**28.** I am obedient and eager to please. _____

**29.** I get angry when people break the rules and get away with it. _____

**30.** I like to keep my room tidy and neat. _____

**31.** I love explaining the whole story to people. _____

**32.** I notice what things people are good at and I tell them. _____

**33.** I like to save money rather than spend it. _____

**34.** I'm good at expressing myself; I love to speak in class. _____

**35.** I enjoy peace and try to avoid conflict. _____

**36.** I tend to be strong-willed and stubborn. _____

**37.** It's hard for me to say no when people ask for my help. _____

**38.** I am very independent. _____

**39.** I love helping people figure out how to solve their problems. _____

**40.** I am good at making money. _____

**41.** I am confident and enthusiastic. _____

**42.** I find it hard to stand up and defend myself. _____

**43.** I want to be obedient and feel guilty when I'm disobedient. _____

**44.** I like doing really nice projects for people. _____

**45.** I think I know more than many of my friends. _____

**46.** I get along well with my parents, neighbors, and friends. _____

**47.** I quickly help when I see a need. _____

**48.** I love leading and organizing when I'm in a group. _____

**49.** I prefer playing in non-competitive sports. _____

To figure out what gift you might have, add up the numbers for the questions listed under each gift below. Then calculate your results.

# PROPHECY (PERCEIVER)

You are able to hear God and deliver a message to others. You may be good at gathering facts and knowing what's the truth and what's not.

**Add the totals for question 1, 8, 15, 22, 29, 36, 43**       **Total = _____**

# SERVING

You love to support a cause by helping others. You may enjoy helping set up snacks for the nursery or cleaning up the church afterwards.

**Add the numbers for questions 2, 9, 16, 23, 30, 37, 44**       **Total= _____**

# TEACHING

You love to learn new things every day and teach others what you've learned. You may like helping with the lessons in Sunday School or Kid's Church.

**Add the numbers for questions 3, 10, 17, 24, 31, 38, 45**       **Total= _____**

# EXHORTATION (ENCOURAGEMENT)

You encourage and guide others toward the right path. You may like greeting on Sunday morning as people arrive.

**Add the numbers for questions 4, 11, 18, 25, 32, 39, 46**       **Total= _____**

# GIVING

You save and create to give to those in need. Maybe you like making offering boxes that kids can use to save coins and bring to church. Or you may run a lemonade stand to raise money for the needy.

**Add the numbers for questions 5, 12, 19, 26, 33, 40, 47     Total= _____**

# LEADERSHIP (ADMINISTRATION)

You set goals and direct others toward those goals. You may be really good at helping with Vacation Bible School at your church. That takes a lot of planning and organizing!

**Add the numbers for questions 6, 13, 20, 27, 34, 41, 48     Total= _____**

# MERCY (COMPASSION)

You feel a compassionate heart of God toward others. You may enjoy visiting shut-ins, spending time with those who are older and cannot come to church. You also might make cards for people in the hospital, telling them they are loved and cared for.

**Add the numbers for questions 7, 14, 21, 28, 35, 42, 49     Total= _____**

---

## WRITE DOWN THE 3 GIFTS THAT HAD THE HIGHEST SCORE:

1 _____

2 _____

3 _____

# DAY 39

## USE YOUR GIFT

### PARABLE OF THE BAGS OF GOLD

In Matthew 25:14-30, Jesus tells a parable about a man leaving on a journey. The man called all of his servants together and gave his wealth to them.

**"To one he gave five bags of gold, to another two bags, and to another one bag, each according to his ability,"** Jesus said in this parable. **"Then he went on his journey."**

When the master returned, the man who received five bags of gold told him, **"Master, you entrusted me with five bags of gold. See, I have gained five more."**

Pleased, the master said, **"Well done, good and faithful servant! You have been faithful with a few things; I will put you in charge of many things."**

The man with two bags of gold told the master he had gained two more. Once again, the master said, **"Well done, good and faithful servant! You have been faithful with a few things; I will put you in charge of many things."**

But when the servant who received one bag came to the Master, things were very different.

"'Master,' he said, 'I knew that you are a hard man, harvesting where you have not sown and gathering where you have not scattered seed. So I was afraid and went out and hid your gold in the ground. See, here is what belongs to you.'

"His master replied, 'You wicked, lazy servant! So you knew that I harvest where I have not sown and gather where I have not scattered seed? Well then, you should have put my money on deposit with the bankers, so that when I returned I would have received it back with interest.'"

In fact, the master was so angry that he took away the man's one bag and gave it to the guy who had ten! Then the man was tossed into the darkness.

Back in the time of Jesus, another word for "gold" or "money" was "talent. " In fact, some Bible translations use the word "talent" instead of "gold" in this story. That's why some people call this the Parable of the Talents.

This can be confusing because when we say "talent" today, we usually mean our gifts and abilities. Because of the different meanings of the word "talent," some people use this parable to talk about how we use our gifts—not only our money.

Jesus is the giver of all gifts and talents. Everyone, from the Olympic athlete and barber to pop singer and truck driver have talents given to them by God. But God wants us to do more than just discover our talents. God wants us to use our talents. In the parable, one servant buried his gold, or talent, instead of using it. That's why the master was so upset.

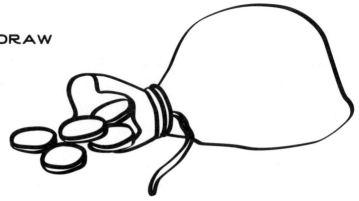

WRITE DOWN OR DRAW
WHAT YOU THINK
YOUR TALENT IS
IN THE BAG
OF GOLD.

# THE BEST FIT

Did you notice that not everyone in the parable was given the same amount of gold? Why did the master give one servant five bags of gold and another servant just one? And why does Jesus give some people many talents and abilities and others just one or two? To answer these questions, look up Matthew 25:15 and finish this sentence: **"To one he gave five bags of gold, to another two bags, and to another one bag, each according to _____ ."**

Jesus knows you inside and out. He knows you BEST. Jesus may not give you the exact same talents or same number of gifts as other people, but Jesus gives you exactly what you need. Also, Jesus doesn't compare you to anyone else.

# PRICELESS!

Back then, a bag of gold, or a "talent," was worth as much money as someone could make in 20 years! In today's money, that would be about one million dollars! So we don't have to feel sorry for the man who received one talent, or a million dollars.

What this tells us is that our talents and abilities are priceless. If you don't believe it, ask someone who lost the ability to walk how much money they'd pay to go for a stroll. They'd probably say they'd pay a million dollars. Walking and running don't seem like million-dollar gifts—until you can't do them any longer. Instead of comparing our gifts and talents to others in our church or community, be thankful for what we have. It's the best fit for us.

# WHAT ARE YOU DOING WITH YOUR GIFTS?

Write down what the master said to the two servants who doubled their amounts.

**THE SERVANT WHO TURNED 5 BAGS INTO 10 BAGS:**

_____

**THE SERVANT WHO TURNED 2 BAGS INTO 4 BAGS:**

_____

The master had the same answer for both servants, even though one of them ended up with many more bags than the other. The master didn't just look at the end result. He looked at what they started with.

Jesus cares about what you're doing with your gifts, but He also knows what you've been given. He knows your challenges. Jesus is more interested in who you are becoming on the inside than all the good things you're doing on the outside.

# CHALLENGE

Look back at the gifts and talents you wrote down in the money bag on page 258. How can you use your gifts and talents at church, home, or school? Write or draw your answer in the box below.

# DAY 40

## CHOOSE CHURCH

# BE A GOOD NEWSIE

## NEWSIES

Before computers, radio, and TV, people in the 1800s got most of their news from newspapers. In many big cities, people would buy the newspaper from poor orphans and runaways who slept on the street and called themselves "newsboys."

The newsboys would buy 100 copies of a newspaper for 50 cents (a half cent per paper) and then sell them on the street for a "penny a paper." For each paper sold, they made a half cent for themselves. They used this money to buy food, clothing, and other things they needed to survive, including more papers.

However, the newspaper owners got greedy and decided to charge the newsboys 60 cents for every 100 papers, rather than 50 cents. Furious, in 1899 the newsboys decided to go on strike, which means they wouldn't work; they wouldn't sell newspapers. They blocked bridges, and more than 5,000 newsboys attended rallies. This famous strike led, a few decades later, to laws that made the newsboys' life much better. The story of the strike was even retold in an old Disney movie called *Newsies*.

Whenever the newsboys sold papers on street corners, they would call out the headlines. However, they discovered a curious thing. Whenever they shouted about scary or bad news, they sold more papers. Some things never change.

## THE GOOD NEWSIES

The newsboys discovered something that remains true today: Bad news sells better than good news. That's why we have the expression, "If it Bleeds, it Leads." News about violent things (and other bad things) becomes the "lead news" of the day. The big headlines.

Good news might not be what people will pay for, but it's what all people need. The best place to hear the best news of all—the Good News of Jesus Christ—is the Church.

And the best news that ever came into the world was when Jesus spilled His blood on the cross to save us. When He bled, He led us to salvation.

## RED ALERT!

One thing that helped the Church grow was its care for the poor and sick. For instance, during a terrible disease epidemic around the year 260 A.D., a man named Dionysius said Christians took care of the sick, putting themselves in great danger. He was amazed.

The Good News of Jesus has affected more people in more places than any other news event in the history of the world. Below, on the "Today's News" newspaper, fill the newspaper page with headlines of today's news in the world. Also, draw pictures of the news. Next, on "The Good News" newspaper, fill the newspaper page with a headline and picture of Good News from the time of Jesus. The first story has already been filled in for you.

**THE GOOD NEWS**

RED LETTER KIDS SEEK GOD'S STRENGTH

I CAN DO ALL THIS THROUGH HIM WHO GIVES ME STRENGTH. (PHILIPPIANS 4:13)

SUMMON YOUR POWER, GOD; SHOW US YOUR STRENGTH, OUR GOD, AS YOU HAVE DONE BEFORE. (PSALMS 68:28)

# CHALLENGE

Invite someone to church—someone you know who does not attend church regularly. The only thing that might be keeping them from coming is an invitation!

# WHAT NOW?

## ONLY THE BEGINNING

Congratulations! You've finished all 40 days and crossed the finish line.
But guess what? This is only the beginning of your quest to follow Jesus.

So far, you've learned that BEING like Jesus means putting His habits
into practice:

- **FORM FRIENDSHIPS**

- **STUDY SCRIPTURE**

- **PAUSE TO PRAY**

- **STOP FOR SOLITUDE**

- **CHOOSE CHURCH**

Here's your final challenge. Pick just ONE of these habits and make it your
main goal. Are you not sure where to start? No worries. We've got you
covered. Check out the following six steps, which turn an activity into a habit.

# 1 WRITE IT DOWN

The habit I want to tackle is...

_____

_____

# 2 BE SPECIFIC

How am I going to make this my habit?

_____

_____

When will I do it?

_____

_____

Where will I do it?

_____

_____

With whom am I going to accomplish this goal?

_____

_____

Why do I want this habit in my life?

_____

_____

**3 TELL SOMEONE ABOUT IT**

I am going to tell _____ about my goal.

**4 KEEP TRACK OF YOUR PROGRESS**

Put a checkmark on each day you complete your goal.

| SUN | MON | TUE | WED | THU | FRI | SAT |
|-----|-----|-----|-----|-----|-----|-----|
|     |     |     |     |     |     |     |

**5 CELEBRATE YOUR VICTORIES**

When I accomplish my goal, my reward or prize will be:

_____

_____

**6 DON'T GIVE UP!**

Some days, meeting your goal will not happen like you were hoping. That's OK. Start again the next day. We're not shooting for perfection. God's grace is made perfect through our weaknesses, failures, and mistakes. So don't worry about your mistakes. God's got grace for you, and it never runs out. He will always be there with a new day and a fresh start.

# "I KEEP MY EYES ALWAYS ON THE LORD. WITH HIM AT MY RIGHT HAND, I WILL NOT BE SHAKEN."

## PSALM 16:8

HAVE FUN COLORING THIS PAGE!
FIND MORE LIKE THIS AT BEINGCHALLENGE.COM/KIDS

# THE SANDS OF REDVALE

## PART 7

"What did you just say?" Aiden whispered to Isabella.

"I asked if you can find a really loud song in that hymnal."

"Oh." Aiden knew exactly what she was getting at. A loud song might just topple the walls of the castle.

"We should probably wait for Red to get out of the dungeon before we start singing loudly," Emily whispered. "We wouldn't want the castle walls to fall on him."

"Good point. We should…" Aiden barely got those words out of his mouth when Red the Fox suddenly threw open the door of the nearby tower. He came sprinting out, as if his tail was on fire. Malachi was right behind, still carrying the trumpet.

From inside the tower came a loud roar, deep and rolling, like distant thunder.

"I don't like the sound of that," said Isabella.

Suddenly, the tower door exploded and a huge dragon busted through, breathing out great blasts of sand. People scattered to all sides, screaming. The Sand Dragon raised its body to a great height and breathed out a torrent of sand, burying some of the soldiers.

"Who dared to awaken my dragon?" shouted the Sand Sovereign.

"Who dared, who dared?" piped up the royal poodle.

"Someone stole my key!" the dragon roared at the people below.

"Who dared to steal my dragon's key?" the king shouted, stepping out into the open courtyard and pointing at the crowd.

"Who dared?" squeaked the royal poodle.

No one spoke up. But Aiden could see that Red was hiding something behind his back.

The king noticed too. "What's that behind your back, fox?"

"Yeah, what's behind your back?" echoed the poodle.

The Sand Dragon turned its mighty head toward poor Red. Aiden realized they had to do something quickly. He began to flip through the hymnal, looking for a really loud song, but so many pages had already turned to sand. He'd be lucky to find any song at all.

"Hurry!" Isabella said. "Just pick something! Anything!"

"How about the Hallelujah Chorus?" Aiden said, finally landing on a page that hadn't turned to sand. It was their parents' favorite hymn, and you couldn't get much louder than the Hallelujah Chorus.

"Let's do it," said Emily.

Aiden cleared his throat and together all three Perez kids began to belt out the words.

*"The kingdom of this world*
*Is become the kingdom of our Lord!*
*And of His Christ, and of His Christ*
*And He shall reign forever and ever!*
*And He shall reign forever and ever*
*Forever and ever, forever and ever!"*

As they sang, Malachi broke out into a big grin. Then he put the trumpet to his lips and began to play along. Aiden saw cracks appear in the castle wall to his left. The loudness of the music also seemed to be scaring the Sand Dragon. The monster pulled back.

"How are you doing that?" a soldier said to Malachi, when he saw him playing the trumpet.

"Don't ask questions! Just play along with me!" Malachi shouted.

Baffled, the guard put his trumpet to his lips and he too began to play. He seemed shocked to hear music coming out of the thing that he once used to shoot sand. But he kept on playing, and large cracks continued to form in the walls of the castle.

Aiden, Emily, and Isabella sang even louder.

*"King of Kings, and Lord of Lords!*
*King of Kings, and Lord of Lords!*
*King of Kings, and Lord of Lords!*
*And Lord of Lords!"*

By this time, the Sand Sovereign was in a rage.

"I told you to stop singing!" he bellowed. "And stop playing those blasted sandblasters!"

"They're called trumpets!" shouted one of the guards. "Aren't they wonderful?"

The Sand Sovereign tried to wrestle the trumpet out of the guard's hands. But two other guards had seen him playing, and they too wanted to see if their sandblasters made music.

Suddenly, there were four trumpets playing. Then a tuba. Then a trombone. And the kids hadn't let up singing.

*"And He shall reign, and He shall reign*
*And He shall reign forever and ever!*
*King of Kings, forever and ever,*
*And Lord of Lords, Hallelujah! Hallelujah!"*

A huge chunk of the castle wall suddenly broke off and crashed to the ground. People ran for cover. The kids kept singing. The trumpets blasted. The Sand Sovereign screamed. The Sand Dragon roared.

"Guards! Stop their music!" the Sand Sovereign commanded.

"Guards, stop them!" the poodle squeaked.

Several guards managed to wrestle the trumpets away from those playing music. Soon, only Malachi was left playing, but several guards pounced on him and tried to take away his trumpet too.

Four guards aimed their sandblasters at Aiden, Isabella, and Emily and told them they had three seconds to stop singing.

What else could they do? The three Perez children ended their song with a whimper. Then all went quiet, and the Sand Sovereign seemed to be in complete control once again. He ordered his Sand Dragon to attack anyone who dared to play music again.

Despite his command…music started to play. But the sound wasn't coming from inside the castle. It was coming from *outside* the castle walls! It started with a single horn. Then two horns, three horns, four, five, six. Pretty soon, it sounded as if an entire army of musicians outside the castle was playing trumpets and trombones and tubas and drums.

Once again, the castle walls began to crack and crumble. A web of cracks formed up and down an entire tower, and then the top came crashing down.

*HOOOOMF!*

Malachi put Red and Emily on Melchior's back and shouted, "Run!"

They sprinted through the inner gatehouse, as walls and towers cracked and crumbled all around them. The music outside the castle walls was deafening, splitting the outer wall. Aiden didn't think he had ever run so fast in his life—not on a baseball or soccer field.

He looked back to see the Sand Dragon right behind them, mouth open, eyes blazing. But when they sprinted through the outer gatehouse and into the wide open spaces, the dragon was struck by a wall of sound.

Gathered around the Sand Castle were two armies of musicians, all of them playing with gusto. The music battered the monster, and it staggered backward. The dragon's entire body trembled under the sound waves hitting it over and over. The dragon screamed and tried to breathe out a blast of sand, but nothing came out. The monster was beginning to crumble. It twisted and collapsed to the ground.

Then, to Aiden's utter amazement, the entire castle behind the dragon began to tremble and shake. With a loud *WHOOOOMF*, the castle collapsed in on itself. Great was its fall.

# THE TRUE KING

Silence.

Everyone and everything went suddenly silent, staring in shock at the fallen castle and dissolved dragon.

"Everyone who hears these words of mine and does not put them into practice is like a foolish man who built his house on sand!" spoke a loud voice. "The rain came down, the streams rose, and the winds blew and beat against that house, and it fell with a great crash."

Those were the words of Jesus, but who was speaking them?

Isabella turned to her left and saw, sitting on a white stallion, the King from Across the Sea. The king of Redvale had come, and he had brought two marching-band armies with him. These were the same musicians that Aiden had met only two days earlier.

"Your majesty," said Isabella, dropping to one knee. Emily, Aiden, Red, Malachi, and Melchior did the same.

"You may rise, sons and daughters," said the True King. "You have done well. Have you found the fifth key? The Church Key?"

In the confusion, Isabella had completely forgotten about the final key.

"I have it," said Red, proudly stepping forward and displaying the golden key.

"And the Sand Box?"

"I have it," said Melchior. Even in all of the excitement, he was still pulling the box behind him on the sled.

"You may insert the final key, children," said the king.

"Me too?" asked Red.

"You too, good and faithful fox."

Aiden, Emily, Isabella, and Red put their hands (and paw) one upon the other, and took hold of the fifth key. Together, they solemnly and carefully inserted the key. At first, it seemed to catch on something. But with a little wiggle, the key slid in smoothly. They turned it. The key CLICKED, and the box's lid popped open, only a couple of inches. It was enough for a rush of wind and light to come pouring out.

"You may fully open it, all four of you."

All of them put their hands (and paw) on the box lid and together they lifted. *What's this?* Isabella thought, staring into the box.

"A rock?" Red said, obviously shocked. Inside the box was nothing more than a large chunk of stone. No wonder the box was so heavy.

"It is not any old rock," said Malachi, stepping up beside them. "It is the Cornerstone."

"The what?" asked Emily.

"The Cornerstone holds a building together," said the king. "All other stones in a building must be aligned with the Cornerstone."

"Oooookay," said Isabella. "But what are we supposed to do with a rock in the middle of a desert? The Sand Castle has fallen. What good is this?"

The king leaned forward on his horse and smiled at Malachi. "You may show the children what to do, Malachi."

"Yes, sire." Malachi motioned to the children. "Follow me."

# THE CORNERSTONE

Malachi turned toward the Sand Castle, which lay in ruins. As they walked through the rubble, they spotted the Sand Sovereign. He seemed to be in a daze, wandering through the huge mounds of sand. His royal poodle was still at his side.

"My castle…" he moaned. When he caught sight of the kids, he pointed a finger and shrieked, "It's all your fault!"

"All your fault!" squeaked the royal poodle.

The Sand Sovereign started to make a move to attack them. But he staggered backward when he saw the Cornerstone being pulled along on the sled.

"You wouldn't dare," the Sand Sovereign said.

"You cannot stop us," Malachi said.

The Sand Sovereign glared, as if he was trying to decide what to do. Then he slowly lowered himself to the ground and started building. The defeated king was trying to build a little sand castle of his own. But the sand wouldn't pack well, and it kept falling to pieces. Isabella felt a bit sorry for him.

Meanwhile, Malachi led them to the only piece of the castle still standing. It was a single wall about three feet wide and four feet high—and it was made out of stone!

"Everyone who hears these words of mine and puts them into practice is like a wise man who built his house on the rock," Malachi said. "The rain came down, the streams rose, and the winds blew and beat against that house; yet it did not fall, because it had its foundation on the rock."

"That's a Bible verse, isn't it?" Emily asked Isabella.

"It is," Isabella said. "It's part of the Parable of the Wise and Foolish Builders."

The stone wall seemed to be missing only one piece. There was a gap, and it looked just the right size to fit the Cornerstone.

"You know what to do," Malachi said to the children and the fox.

"But this is going to be too heavy for us to lift," Isabella said.

"Try it. You'll be surprised."

All four of them—Emily, Aiden, Isabella, and Red—took hold of the Cornerstone and raised it up. Isabella was shocked. Had they gotten stronger in Redvale, or was the stone strangely light? They slid the rock into place in the wall.

"I suggest we stand back," Malachi said.

The kids did as he said because something strange was beginning to happen. The ground was starting to shake, like an earthquake.

"Quickly now," said Malachi, and they ran as fast as they could, all the way back to the True King. Then they turned and watched. Something was growing, something was rising from the ground, like a fast-growing plant. Could it be? A castle was rising from the ground, cracking through sand.

The Sand Sovereign also saw what was happening, and he got out of the way just in time. A full-grown castle burst out of the ground and shot up into the sky, its stone looking as fresh as the day it was cut. The castle was huge, and twelve flags fluttered from its ramparts.

"Let me guess what those twelve flags are," said Aiden.

"The flags of the twelve disciples," added Emily.

"You got it," said Malachi.

"By the way, what was the twelfth flag where you found the key?" Isabella asked Red.

"I don't know. I only know that the flag had the picture of a Bible and sword on it."

"It's the flag of Matthias," said Malachi.

"Matthias?" said Emily. "Which one was he?"

"He was the disciple who took Judas's place after Judas betrayed Jesus," Melchior explained. "He was well-versed in Scripture—just like Isabella."

"When the disciples lost one of their twelve, they were left with a missing piece," Malachi added. "Matthias was that missing piece."

"You have all come a long way," said the True King, drawing up beside them on his horse. He dismounted and approached. "Isabella, you learned to build your faith on Scripture—and not to be afraid about what others think."

The king draped a necklace over her head. On the necklace, there dangled the Scripture Key, which she had retrieved.

"Aiden, you learned that prayer is like beautiful music, praising God and guiding our steps." The king draped him with a necklace that carried the Prayer Key.

"And Emily, you discovered that by spending time in solitude with God, your faith will grow as strong as a tree." With those words, he draped her with a necklace carrying the Solitude Key. "Keep these keys ever with you, to remind you what's most important. These are the keys to life."

Emily noticed that Red looked a bit left out. "And what about Red, your majesty? And Melchior?"

"Don't worry, I would never forget them."

The king leaned down low to drape Red with a necklace that carried the Church Key. "Red, you showed that you have the heart of Peter, the rock. You also showed that the Church is built on the solid rock, who is Jesus."

The king turned toward Melchior and grinned. "Last but not least, Melchior you have been a loyal and steady friend, every step of the way. You carried the Cornerstone mile after mile, and you put the needs of your friends ahead of your own. You have earned the Friendship Key."

By this time, Melchior was blubbering, overflowing with tears. "It's a good thing we camels store a lot of water in our bodies. I'm losing gallons with all of my crying."

"That's all five keys," said Emily. "Isn't there one left over for Malachi?"

Malachi crouched down low and gave Emily a hug. "Thanks, but my reward has been traveling with all of you once again. I loved seeing you grow—strengthening friendships with each other, reading Scripture, building your faith on the rock, and spending time in solitude and prayer. When you return home, use these habits to connect with God…and with each other."

"Would you like to be the first to enter the new castle?" the True King asked the kids.

Emily sensed what lay ahead. "This is the end of our journey, isn't it?"

"For now," said the king. "Redvale may need you again someday."

"And we may need Redvale again," said Isabella. "I promise I won't ever be afraid to talk about Redvale when we return home. I don't care what people say or think. I love this place. And I love you."

There were hugs all around and plenty more tears. Even the Sand Sovereign wandered up to them, obviously very moved. He had tears in his eyes.

"This is so beautiful," he said, blowing his nose.

"So beautiful," squeaked the royal poodle, blowing her nose.

Red borrowed the Sand Sovereign's handkerchief, and he too blew his nose about five times.

"Don't worry, I'll wash it," he told the Sand Sovereign.

"Just keep it."

Before the kids turned to leave, the True King got back on his horse and said: "And now these three remain: faith, hope and love. But the greatest of these is love."

"Faith, hope, and love is the ultimate three-part harmony," Malachi said, giving each of the kids one final hug. "So keep on singing together. You are brother and sister, but you are also friends. Remember that."

"We wiiiiiiill," sang Isabella.

"We wiiiiiiill," sang Emily, striking a higher note.

"We wiiiiiiill," sang Aiden, striking a lower note.

Perfect harmony.

Malachi handed the trumpet to Aiden, and then the three Perez children strode through the outer gatehouse, where guards played a trumpet fanfare for them. Then they passed through the inner gatehouse with music ringing in their ears.

And just like that, they were home. They were back in Emily's closet, walking toward the light. They stepped out into Emily's room, and none of them seemed to know what to say or do. Did all of that just happen?

Emily's room was still a mess.

"We can help you clean," Isabella said, beginning to sort through the things piled up on Emily's bed.

"Thanks. Let's tackle all of our rooms," said Emily. "Together."

"We just took down a Sand Dragon," Aiden added, setting aside his trumpet. "I think we can handle a few messy rooms."

As they began to work, Isabella was the first to begin singing. Then Aiden and Emily joined in, completing the three-part harmony. Their voices didn't sound as beautiful as they did in Redvale, but that was okay. They still sounded better singing together than alone.

For the rest of the day, their house rang with music.

# – THE END –

# ABOUT
# THE
# AUTHORS

**Zach Zehnder** is a husband, father, speaker, author, and pastor. His life mission is to challenge people of all ages to become greater followers of Jesus. Zach continues to seek new and innovative ways to share the Gospel with the world, from raising money to buy a recovery house by breaking a Guinness World Record for the Longest Speech Marathon to paying for the church logo to be tattooed on church members. In 2017, Zach wrote the bestselling book *Red Letter Challenge* and together with his wife Allison, co-wrote *Red Letter Challenge Kids*. Since then, they have co-founded a ministry under the name Red Letter Challenge and continue to write books and speak about the importance of following Jesus.

**Allison Zehnder** was raised in West Togo, Africa, as a missionary kid. Moving back to the United States, she graduated from Concordia University Wisconsin with a degree in Theology and minor in Missions and Youth Ministry. Along with Zach, she moved to Mount Dora, Florida, and served as Children's Director for 5 years at theCross Church. She is co-author of *Red Letter Challenge Kids* and currently assists in other writing projects for Red Letter Challenge as well as raising their two children, Nathan and Brady.

**Doug Peterson** is the Gold-Medallion-winning author of 70 books, including 42 for the popular VeggieTales series and four historical novels. He is the co-storywriter for the best-selling VeggieTales video, *Larry-Boy and the Rumor Weed*, and recently worked as head writer on six comic books in *The Legends of Lightfall* series. Doug has also been a writer for the University of Illinois since 1979, and he lives in Champaign, Illinois, with his wife, Nancy. They have two grown sons. You can find Doug online at www.bydougpeterson.com, or on Facebook under "Doug Peterson Author."

# DID YOU KNOW YOU CAN TAKE ON THE CHALLENGE WITH YOUR WHOLE CHURCH?

## ALL-IN, TURN-KEY SERMON SERIES WITH PROVEN RESULTS!

## WANT YOUR PASTOR TO RECEIVE A FREE COPY?
### EMAIL HELLO@REDLETTERCHALLENGE.COM